Around the World in Eighty Days

Jules Verne

OXFORD
UNIVERSITY PRESS

OXFORD

UNIVERSITY PRESS

Oxford University Press is a department of the University of Oxford.
It furthers the University's objective of excellence in research, scholarship,
and education by publishing worldwide in

Oxford New York

Auckland Cape Town Dar es Salaam Hong Kong Karachi
Kuala Lumpur Madrid Melbourne Mexico City Nairobi
New Delhi Shanghai Taipei Toronto

With offices in

Argentina Austria Brazil Chile Czech Republic France Greece
Guatemala Hungary Italy Japan South Korea Poland Portugal
Singapore Switzerland Thailand Turkey Ukraine Vietnam

Oxford is a registered trade mark of Oxford University Press

Illustrated by Choy Man Yung

Syllabus design and text analysis by David Foulds

ISBN: 978-0-19-597143-9

Printed in Hong Kong
Published by Oxford University Press (China) Ltd
18th Floor, Warwick House East, Taikoo Place, 979 King's Road, Quarry Bay
Hong Kong

Contents

Introduction

*A*round *the World in Eighty Days* is a story about travel and adventure. It is set in the nineteenth century. At that time, there were no aeroplanes. It was slow and difficult to travel.

In the story the main character, Phileas Fogg, believes that it is possible to travel around the world in eighty days. He bets his friends twenty thousand pounds that he will be able to do it. His new servant, Passepartout, goes with him on the tour of the world. Mr Fogg and Passepartout travel by different kinds of transport: steamships, railways, sledges, and even elephants! They visit Egypt, India, Hong Kong, Japan and America. They have lots of exciting adventures in these places. In India, they risk their lives to save a beautiful princess.

Around the World in Eighty Days is a very popular story. It has been made into films many times. Jackie Chan starred in the 2004 version. The challenge of travelling around the world in eighty days has interested people for many years. In 1889, journalist Nellie Bly managed to make the journey in seventy-two days. She wrote about her adventures in a newspaper, the *New York World*. In 1988, the actor Michael Palin took on the same challenge. He travelled around the world without using an aircraft. He completed his journey before the deadline. He recorded his adventures for a TV programme, also called *Around the World in Eighty Days*.

Now read where this great adventure first started …

Important people in the story

Phileas Fogg
A rich Englishman who lives alone and who is exact about everything.

Jean Passepartout
A brave, young Frenchman who works for Mr Fogg.

Detective Fix
A detective who wants to catch Mr Fogg because he thinks that he is a bank robber.

Mrs Aouda
An Indian princess who needs saving.

About Jules Verne

Jules Verne was born in France in 1828. His father, who was a lawyer, sent him to Paris to study law when he was nineteen. But he did not become a lawyer because he was more interested in writing. He continued to write until he died in 1905.

Jules Verne wrote many travel stories, including *A Journey to the Centre of the Earth* (1864), *From the Earth to the Moon* (1865), *Twenty Thousand Leagues Under the Sea* (1870) and *Around the World in Eighty Days* (1873). His novels were very popular and he became very rich. He bought a boat and sailed around Europe in it.

1
An Impossible Journey

The new servant

In the year 1872, Phileas Fogg lived at Number 7 Saville Row, Burlington Gardens. He was a well-known member of a famous London club called the Reform Club. 5

No one knew very much about Phileas Fogg, except that he was a very polite man and a perfect gentleman. He was an Englishman, but probably did not come from London.

Was Phileas Fogg rich? Yes, but no one could say 10 how he had made his money. Certainly it did not seem quite right to ask Mr Fogg how he had made it. He did not waste his money on foolish things, but he was not mean with it either. If money was needed for poor people, he gave it, but he gave it quietly. 15

Had he travelled? It was probable, for no one knew the world better than he. Whenever any place was mentioned, he seemed to know something about it.

Phileas Fogg had not been away from London for many years. Those who knew him best said that he 20 always went to his club every day and that he always arrived there by exactly the same route at exactly the same time. His only hobbies were reading the newspapers and playing whist. He often won at this quiet game. He always gave away the money that he 25 won. It was clear that Mr Fogg played because he liked playing, and not because he wanted to win.

Phileas Fogg did not have either a wife or any children. Nor did he have any relatives or close friends. He lived alone in his house in Saville Row, where 30

nobody visited him. He had only one servant. He had his breakfast and dinner at the Club. He always had his meals at the same time every day, in the same room, at the same table. No one ever ate with him. He returned
5 home at exactly midnight, to go to bed.

The Saville Row house was not too big, but it was very comfortable and well ordered. Phileas Fogg did not like anything to go wrong in his house. But the day this story begins, 2nd October, something had gone
10 wrong, and Phileas Fogg had dismissed his servant. He was now sitting in his armchair looking at the man who hoped to become his new servant.

'You say you are French?' Phileas Fogg asked him.

15 'Yes, sir,' replied the man, 'but I have lived in England for some time. My name is Jean Passepartout. I have
20 come here in the hope of living quietly with you.'

'I have heard good things about you,' replied Mr Fogg. 'You know how I like to live?'

25 'Yes, sir.'

'Well, what is the time, then?'

'It is twenty-two minutes past eleven,' replied Passepartout, taking his watch out of his pocket. It was a very large silver watch.

30 'You are slow,' said Mr Fogg.

'Pardon me, sir, but that's impossible.'

'You are four minutes slow. It does not matter, now that you know. Now, from this moment, twenty-six minutes past eleven, this Wednesday morning, 2nd
35 October 1872, you are my servant.'

Passepartout is pleased

Then Phileas Fogg rose, placed his hat upon his head, and went out without another word. Passepartout heard the street door close.

During the few minutes that he had seen Phileas Fogg, Passepartout had examined his future master carefully. He was a man who might be forty years old. He had a fine, handsome face.

Phileas Fogg was an exact man. He was never in a hurry. He never wasted his time. Whenever he went anywhere, he always took the shortest route. He never made any unnecessary action or movement. No one had ever seen him look upset.

Jean Passepartout had always been looking for a master that he could serve happily. He was a good man and had a pleasing appearance. He had blue eyes, rosy cheeks and brown, untidy hair.

It is odd that two people who seemed to be so different thought that they would be happy together. Passepartout now wanted to live a quiet, peaceful and orderly life. He expected to find this with Phileas Fogg.

At half past eleven, then, Passepartout found himself alone in the house. He immediately decided to examine it from top to bottom. After looking in all the rooms, and seeing how peaceful, comfortable and well organized the house was, Passepartout rubbed his hands. His face brightened, and he repeated cheerfully, 'This suits me! Mr Fogg and I will understand each other perfectly!'

The gentleman robber

That evening, after Phileas Fogg had had his dinner at the Reform Club, a number of members of the Club came into the room where he was sitting. They were all rich and respectable men. Andrew Stuart was an engineer. John Sullivan and Samuel Fallentin were bankers. Thomas Flanagan and Gauthier Ralph were both important men at the Bank of England.

'Well, Ralph,' said Thomas Flanagan, 'what do you
5 think about that robbery?'

'I think,' replied Andrew Stuart, 'the bank will lose the money.'

'I certainly hope not,' said Gauthier Ralph. 'I am sure we will catch the robber. Very skilful detectives have
10 been sent to America and Europe, to all the major ports, so it will be very difficult for the man to escape.'

'But do you have a description of the robber?' asked Andrew Stuart.

'Well,' said Gauthier Ralph, 'he is not a robber.'
15 'What on earth do you mean? He is not a robber! He has just stolen fifty-five thousand pounds!'

'The newspapers describe him as a gentleman.'

It was Phileas Fogg who had just spoken. He looked out from behind his newspaper. At the same time he
20 greeted his friends, and they greeted him in return. The subject everyone was talking about, and which was in every newspaper, had happened three days before, 29th September. The money had been taken from the desk of the chief clerk of the Bank of England.

25 Once the robbery was known, some of the most skilful detectives were asked to search for the robber. There was a large reward offered if any one of them was successful in catching the robber and returning the money. The reward was two thousand pounds plus five
30 per cent of the money recovered.

As the newspapers said, there was good reason to think that the robber was not an ordinary thief. On 29th September, a well-dressed gentleman had been noticed going in and out of the paying room, which was where the robbery had taken place. A fairly accurate description was therefore made, and it was sent to all the detectives in England and Europe. Some hopeful people, especially Gauthier Ralph and Thomas Flanagan, believed that they had good reason to expect that the robber would not escape. Andrew Stuart did not agree with these hopeful people.

They continued to talk about the bank robbery even after they had all sat down for their game of whist.

'I am sure,' said Stuart, 'that the robber has a good chance of escaping. He must be a very clever man.'

'Well,' said Ralph, 'where can he go safely, now that every country has been warned to watch for him?'

'I am sure the world is big enough to hide him,' said Andrew Stuart.

'It was before,' said Phileas Fogg in a low voice.

'What do you mean?' asked Stuart. 'Has the world now grown smaller?'

'It certainly has,' said Ralph. 'I agree with Mr Fogg. We can now go round the world ten times quicker than it was possible one hundred years ago. And so you see, we will be able to search for our robber very quickly.'

'Mr Ralph,' said Stuart, 'how can you say that the world has grown smaller, just because it now only takes three months to go round it?'

'It only takes eighty days,' said Phileas Fogg.

'Yes, gentlemen,' agreed John Sullivan, 'eighty days, since the new railway across India has been opened.'

'That's right!' said Andrew Stuart. 'But if one met with any bad weather, difficult winds, shipwrecks and train accidents, it would not be possible.'

'I disagree,' replied Phileas Fogg, 'I am sure it could be done.'

The bet

'I would very much like to see you do it!' said Stuart.

5   'Well, let us go together,' said Phileas Fogg.

'Good heavens! I can't,' replied Stuart, 'but I will happily bet four thousand pounds that such a journey, made in eighty days, is impossible.'

'I think it is quite possible,' replied Mr Fogg.

10   'Well, make it then!'

'The tour of the world in eighty days?'

'Yes!'

'I am willing.'

'When?'

15   'At once.'

'This is madness!' cried Stuart. 'Stop this useless talk. Let us play cards properly instead.'

They began to play again, but not for long.

Andrew Stuart looked up from his cards and said, 20 'Well, Mr Fogg, I will bet you four thousand pounds!'

'My dear Stuart,' said Fallentin, 'you cannot be serious!'

'When I say "I bet",' replied Andrew Stuart, 'it is always serious.'

25   'Very well,' said Mr Fogg. He turned to face his companions and said, 'I have twenty thousand pounds in the Baring Brothers Bank. I will willingly bet that.'

'Twenty thousand pounds!' cried John Sullivan. 'And if you are delayed you will lose all that?'

30   'I will not lose,' said Phileas Fogg quietly.

'You are joking!' said Sullivan.

'A good Englishman never jokes when he is making a bet,' replied Phileas Fogg. 'I will bet twenty thousand pounds against anyone that I will make the tour of the world in eighty days or less. Do you accept?'

'We accept,' replied all his companions, after talking among themselves.

'Very well,' said Mr Fogg. 'The Dover train leaves at nine o'clock. I shall be on it.'

'You mean tonight?' asked Stuart.

'I do,' replied Phileas Fogg. 'And since today is Wednesday, 2nd October, I ought to be back in London, in the Reform Club, on Saturday, 21st December, at nine o'clock in the evening. If I am not, my twenty thousand pounds at Baring Brothers will belong to you.'

The tour begins

Passepartout was very surprised to see his master home so early. He was even more surprised when he heard him say:

'We leave in ten minutes for Dover and France.'

Passepartout did not seem to understand.

'You are going to leave home?'

'Yes,' replied Phileas Fogg. 'We are going to make the tour of the world.'

Passepartout could not believe his ears.

'The tour of the world?' he said stupidly.

'In eighty days,' replied Mr Fogg. 'So we have not a moment to lose. We will not take much baggage. Only two changes of clothing. We will buy what else we need on the way. Go and get it ready.'

Passepartout would have liked to make a reply. He could not. He left Mr Fogg and went to his own room. There he fell into a chair.

'And I wanted a quiet life!' he said to himself.

By eight o'clock both Mr Fogg and his servant were ready.

Mr Fogg made sure that he had his general guide to railways and steamships. He also slipped into his bag an enormous package of banknotes. He then handed the bag to Passepartout. 'Take good care of that,' he said. 'It has twenty thousand pounds in it.'

The master and servant then left the Saville Row house, locking it carefully behind them. They reached the railway station at twenty past eight. Mr Fogg gave his servant the money to buy two first-class tickets to Paris. Then, looking round the station, Mr Fogg noticed his five friends from the Reform Club.

'Gentlemen, I am going,' he said, 'and I will have my passport stamped at each country I visit, so that when I return you will know where I have been.'

'Oh! Mr Fogg,' replied Gauthier Ralph, 'that is not necessary. You are a gentleman.'

'I think it is better if I do so,' replied Mr Fogg. 'I will be back in eighty days. Saturday, 21st December, 1872, at nine o'clock in the evening. Goodbye, gentlemen.'

At five minutes to nine, Phileas Fogg and his servant took their seats on the train. At nine o'clock the whistle sounded, and the train started.

Then Passepartout cried out in horror!

'What is the matter?' asked Mr Fogg.

'Well, in — in the rush — I forgot — '

'Forgot what?'

'To turn off the gaslight in my room.'

'Well,' said Mr Fogg coldly, 'you will have to pay the bill when we return.'

2

Is Mr Fogg the Bank Robber?

Detective Fix and the British Consul

At Suez, in Egypt, on Wednesday, 9th October, at eleven o'clock in the morning, the steamship *Mongolia* was expected. It was a very fast ship and nearly always arrived early. Two men were walking up and down by the harbour, waiting at the side of the harbour for the ship to come in. One of these was the British Consul at Suez. The other was a small thin man who had a quiet, thoughtful face. He looked nervous, and seemed to be unable to remain on one spot for more than a few seconds at a time.

The name of this second man was Fix. He was one of the detectives working for the British police to find the man who had robbed the Bank of England of fifty-five thousand pounds. Fix was supposed to watch, with the greatest care, all travellers taking the Suez route. If any one of them looked suspicious, he was to follow him until a warrant of arrest arrived. Just two days before, Fix had received the description of the supposed robber from the English police. The description was that of the well-dressed gentleman who had been noticed in the paying room of the bank. The detective was very excited by the large reward promised in case of success.

'And you say, Consul,' he asked for the tenth time, 'this ship will not be late?'

'No, Mr Fix,' replied the Consul. 'Be patient. But really I do not see how, with the description that you have received, you could recognize your man, even if he is on board the *Mongolia*.'

'Consul,' replied Fix, 'we detectives feel these people rather than know them. It is a special sense using hearing, sight and smell. I have arrested more than one of these gentlemen, and, if my robber is on board, I am
5 certain that he will not slip through my fingers.'

'I hope you're right, Mr Fix, for it was a very large robbery.'

'It was indeed,' replied the detective. 'Fifty-five thousand pounds! We don't often see or hear of such a
10 large amount!'

'Well, Mr Fix,' replied the Consul, 'I do hope you succeed, but I repeat that it will be difficult. Don't you see that the description you have received of this robber fits that of an honest man exactly?'

15 'Consul,' replied the detective, 'great robbers always look like honest people.'

In the meantime, the harbour had become much busier. More and more people were arriving to meet the steamship. Moving among this crowd, Fix was
20 carefully examining all the people who came near him with quick, sharp looks.

It was then half past ten.

'Oh, this ship will never arrive!' he cried when he heard the clock in the town striking.

25 'Don't be so impatient. She cannot be far away now,' replied the Consul.

'How long will she stop in Suez?' asked Fix.

'Only four hours.'

'And from Suez this ship goes to Bombay, in India,
30 and nowhere else?'

'Yes.'

'Well then,' said Fix, 'if the robber has taken this route and this ship, he must plan to get off in Suez and go on somewhere else. He will not want to go to India,
35 because the British are there.'

'Unless he is very clever,' replied the Consul. 'Perhaps he knows that is the last place anyone would think of looking for him.'

After saying this, the Consul returned to his office, which was only a short distance from the harbour.

A man with a passport

Fix did not have to wait much longer. As the town clock struck eleven, the ship arrived. There were quite a number of passengers on board. Some remained on deck, but most of them came ashore in the small boats that had gone out to greet the *Mongolia*.

Fix carefully examined all those who landed. Then one of them approached him. The man asked him very politely if he could show him the office of the British Consul. And at the same time this passenger showed Fix a passport, which he clearly wanted to have stamped. Fix took the passport that was held towards him. He looked quickly at the description written in it. It was exactly the same as the description of the robber he had received from the Chief of Police in London.

'Isn't this passport yours?' he said to the passenger.

'No,' the man replied, 'it is my master's.'

'Where is your master?'

'He remained on board the ship.'

'But,' continued the detective, 'he must go himself to the Consul's office to prove that this is his passport.'

'And where is the office?'

'Over on that corner,' replied the detective, pointing to a house about two hundred feet away.

'Then I must go and fetch my master. He will not like having his plans upset!'

Then the passenger bowed to Fix and returned on board the ship. The detective left the harbour and went to the Consul's office.

'Consul,' he said when he arrived, 'I have strong reasons for believing that our man is aboard the *Mongolia*.' Then Fix told him how he had met the man's servant and seen the man's passport.

'But perhaps he won't come to my office at all,' replied the Consul. 'It is not necessary, you know, to have a British passport stamped in British-controlled lands. Why should the robber want his passport stamped? It only shows that he has been here, and that will not help him to hide from the police.'

'Consul,' replied the detective, 'if he is a clever man he will come.'

'Why?'

'His passport will all be in order, and that will make everyone think he is an honest man. Then we can trick him. You must refuse to stamp his passport.'

'I cannot do that. If his passport is in order, I must stamp it.'

'But Consul, I must keep this man here until I have received a warrant from London.'

'Ah, Mr Fix, that is your business,' replied the Consul, 'but I cannot refuse ...'

Just then there was a knock on the door of the Consul's office, and the office boy brought in two passengers from the *Mongolia*, one of whom was the servant who had been talking to the detective.

Mr Fogg has his passport stamped

The master handed his passport to the Consul, asking him to stamp it. The Consul took the passport and read

it carefully. Fix was standing in one corner of the room,
staring straight at the stranger. He would
never forget his face.

When the Consul had
finished reading, he asked,
'You are Phileas Fogg?'

'Yes, sir,' replied the gentleman.

'And this man is your servant?'

'Yes, this is Mr Passepartout.
He is French.'

'You come from London?'

'Yes.'

'And you are
going where?'

'To Bombay.'

The Consul then stamped the passport. Mr Fogg
paid the necessary fee, then he bowed coldly and left,
followed by Passepartout.

'Well?' asked the detective.

'He looks just like an honest man!' replied the Consul.   20

'Possibly,' replied Fix, 'but that is not the point.
Don't you agree he looks just like the description of the
robber that I have received?'

'I agree, but you know that all descriptions --'

'I am sure I am right,' interrupted Fix. 'I think the   25
servant will be a great help to me. He cannot stop
talking. I will see you again soon, Consul.'

In the meantime Mr Fogg returned to the *Mongolia*.
Passepartout did not go on board immediately. He was
walking round the harbour when Fix found him.   30

Fix questions Passepartout

'Well, my friend,' said Fix, coming up to him, 'is your
master's passport stamped?'

'Ah! it is you, sir,' replied the Frenchman. 'Thank you for your help earlier. Yes, everything is in order.'

'And are you looking at the country?'

'Yes, but we go very soon. It seems to me as if I am travelling in a dream. So this is Suez?'

'Yes, it is in Egypt.'

'And in Africa?'

'Yes, in Africa.'

'In Africa,' repeated Passepartout. 'I cannot believe it. I did not think we would go further than Paris! I thought I would see so much of my dear city, but we were only there from twenty past seven till twenty to nine in the morning. And it rained all that time!'

'You are in a great hurry, then?' asked the detective.

'No, I am not, but my master is. I mustn't forget to buy some shirts and shoes! We left London with only a small bag each.'

'I will take you to a shop where you will find everything you want.'

As they walked towards the shop, Passepartout never stopped talking.

'The most important thing is that I don't miss the ship,' said Passepartout.

'You have plenty of time,' replied Fix, 'it is only noon!' Passepartout pulled out his large watch.

'Noon,' he said. 'It is eight minutes to ten!'

'Your watch is slow!' replied Fix.

'My watch! This watch used to belong to my great-grandfather! It doesn't even lose five minutes a year.'

'I see what has happened,' replied Fix. 'Your watch is still telling London time, which is about two hours slower than Suez. You must be careful to set your watch at noon in each new country.'

'What! I will never touch my watch,' cried Passepartout.

After a few moments, Fix said to him, 'You left London very suddenly, then?'

'I should say so! Last Wednesday, at eight o'clock in the evening, Mr Fogg returned from his club, and three quarters of an hour after that we had started our journey.'

'Where is your master going, then?'

'He is making the tour of the world!'

'The tour of the world!' cried Fix.

'Yes, in eighty days! He has made a bet, he says. But, between ourselves, I do not believe it. It would be madness. There must be something else.'

'Is this Mr Fogg clever?'

'I should think so.'

'Is he rich?'

'He seems to be. He has brought a lot of money with him for this trip. He's not afraid to spend it, either. He has promised the engineer of the *Mongolia* a large reward if he can get the ship to Bombay a few days early.'

'And you have known him for a long time, this master of yours?'

'I,' replied Passepartout, 'became his servant the very same day that we left London.'

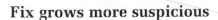

Fix grows more suspicious

These answers gave the detective plenty to think about.

The plan to leave London so soon after the robbery; the large amount of money carried with them; the speed of travel from one country to another; all these things could only make Fix believe more and more that he was right about Mr Fogg.

Fix kept talking to the Frenchman, and learnt for certain that this man did not know his master at all. He learnt that Phileas Fogg lived alone in London, that he was known to be rich, but that no one knew where his money had come from. Everyone thought that he was a mysterious man. At the same time, Fix believed what Passepartout had told him: that Phileas Fogg really was going to Bombay.

'Is Bombay far from here?' asked Passepartout.

'Quite far,' replied the detective. 'It will take you more than ten days by sea.'

'And where is Bombay?'

'It is in India.'

Fix left Passepartout at the shop. He then rushed back to the Consul's office.

'Sir,' he said to the Consul, 'I have my man. He is pretending to be a little strange, a person who is making the tour of the world in eighty days.'

Fix then told the Consul what he had learnt from Passepartout.

'Well,' said the Consul, 'it seems that you are probably right. What are you going to do?'

'I shall send a telegram to London asking for a warrant to arrive in Bombay as soon as possible. Then I will sail on the *Mongolia*, with this Mr Fogg, to India. There, on British soil, I will be able to arrest him.'

Mr Fix said goodbye to the Consul and went to the telegram office. As soon as he had sent his telegram, he went to get himself ready to sail on the *Mongolia*. A quarter of an hour later, with a large bag in his hand, and well supplied with money, Fix got on board the *Mongolia*. Soon the fast steamship was going as quickly as she could down the Red Sea.

3
India

The warrant has not arrived

The *Mongolia* arrived at Bombay on 20th October, two days early. During the voyage, Passepartout and Mr Fix had seen quite a lot of each other and had become very friendly. Mr Fogg had been able to play his favourite game of whist with some of the other passengers.

The passengers of the *Mongolia* left the ship and arrived in Bombay at half past four in the afternoon. The train which would take Phileas Fogg and his servant across India was leaving for Calcutta at eight o'clock that same evening.

As soon as they had left the ship, Phileas Fogg told Passepartout to go and buy some things for him. He then made his way as quickly as possible towards the passport office. He did not think of looking at any of the sights of Bombay, not the city hall, nor the huge library, the famous forts, the harbour and the local markets. He was not interested in anything like that. After leaving the passport office, with his passport stamped, he went straight to the railway station.

Detective Fix left the *Mongolia* just after Mr Fogg. He went to speak to the Chief of Police in Bombay. He asked if the warrant of arrest had been received from London, but no one knew anything about it.

Fix was rather upset. He asked the Chief if he could give him a warrant for the arrest of Mr Fogg. The Chief refused. Mr Fogg had done nothing wrong in India. Fix had to wait for the warrant to come from London. The only thing he could do was to make sure that he did not

lose his robber while he was in Bombay. Fix was certain
that Mr Fogg would stay in Bombay, which would give
the warrant time to arrive.

Passepartout, too, had thought that his master would
5   finally end his travels in Bombay, but after the last
orders which his master had given him, he realized he
was wrong. Mr Fogg had told him to make sure that he
did not miss the eight o'clock train to Calcutta.
Passepartout realized that even Calcutta would
10   probably not be the last stop. He began to ask himself if,
after all, the bet that Mr Fogg had made was serious.

After Passepartout had done his shopping, he
decided to walk through the streets of Bombay.
Everything seemed new and wonderful to him. One
15   thing in particular caught his attention: a beautiful
Hindu temple. He decided to go inside. Unfortunately
he did not know that Christians are not allowed in
Hindu temples, and that the Hindus themselves must
take their shoes off before they go in.

20   Passepartout walked innocently into the temple.
Suddenly he was thrown onto the floor by three priests.
They were very angry. They tore off his shoes and socks
and started to beat him. The Frenchman was very
strong. He got to his feet again and rushed out of the
25   temple as quickly as he could.

At five to eight, just a
few moments before the
train left, Passepartout
arrived at the station.
30   He had lost his hat
and was without
shoes and socks.
He had also
lost his parcel
35   of shopping.

Detective Fix was also at the railway station. He had followed Phileas Fogg to the station and realized that his robber was going to leave Bombay. He immediately decided that he must leave too, and follow Fogg all the way to Calcutta, and further, if necessary. Passepartout 5 did not see Fix when he arrived at the station, but Fix heard him tell his master what had happened to him.

'I hope it will not happen to you again,' was all Phileas Fogg replied. Then he took his seat in the train. The poor man, looking rather upset, and having no 10 shoes or socks, followed his master without another word. Fix was going to get his seat, when a thought stopped him, and he suddenly changed his plans.

'No, I will stay in Bombay,' he said to himself. 'A wrong has been done in British-controlled India. I have 15 caught my man.'

At this moment the train gave a sharp whistle and disappeared into the darkness. It had started on time.

The General

Passepartout was seated in the same part of the train as 20 his master. A third traveller was in the opposite corner.

It was Sir Francis Cromarty, one of the people Mr Fogg had played whist with on the voyage from Suez to Bombay. He was a general in the Indian Army.

Sir Francis Cromarty was tall, fair, and about fifty 25 years old. He had lived in India nearly all his life and knew it as well as any of the local people. He knew a great deal about the history and the customs of the different parts of India.

Sir Francis Cromarty had noticed the cleverness of 30 his travelling companion. Of all the strange people that the General had met, no one was quite like Phileas Fogg.

Mr Fogg had told Sir Francis about his plan for the tour round the world in eighty days.

'You just might have a problem about what happened to your servant, Mr Fogg,' said the General.
5 'The British Government is very careful to punish those who upset the priests of the Hindu religion. And so they should be, too — it is one of the best ways to keep peace in this country. The Government therefore insists above all things,' went on Sir Francis, 'that the religious
10 customs of the Hindus shall be respected, and if your servant had been caught — '

'Yes, if he had been caught, Sir Francis,' replied Mr Fogg, 'he would have been punished, probably by being sent to jail, and then once that was done, he
15 would have quietly returned to Europe. I do not see how the matter could have delayed his master!'

At this the conversation stopped again.

The next day, when Passepartout woke up, he found it difficult to remember where he was. Outside, the
20 Indian countryside flew by. He could hardly believe it was real. At half past twelve, the train stopped at a village station. Passepartout was able to buy a pair of Indian slippers. They were decorated with false pearls, and Passepartout put them on proudly. The travellers
25 ate a quick lunch and then the train started again.

Passepartout's thoughts

It is a good time to mention now what Passepartout was thinking. Until he had arrived in Bombay, he had thought that everything would stop there. But now that
30 he was hurrying at full speed across India, his mind had changed. He felt again his interest in travelling. He began to take his master's plans seriously. He believed in the bet, and therefore the tour of the world, and that

it must be done in eighty days and not more. Already he was upset by possible delays and the accidents that might happen along the route. He felt interested in the bet and felt very bad about what had happened to him in the temple. He might have lost the bet for Mr Fogg!

The next day was 22nd October. Sir Francis asked Passepartout what the time was. Passepartout told him that it was three o'clock in the morning. In fact, this famous watch, which always told London time, was now four hours slower that it should have been.

Sir Francis then told Passepartout the right time, and added the same remark that Passepartout had already heard from Fix. It was useless, nothing Sir Francis could say would persuade Passepartout to change his watch. He always kept it on London time.

The train can go no further

At eight o'clock in the morning the train stopped unexpectedly in the middle of nowhere. A few huts could be seen on one side. The conductor went along calling out, 'The passengers will get out here!'

Phileas Fogg looked at Sir Francis Cromarty, who did not appear to understand why the train had stopped and everyone had to get out. Passepartout was also surprised. He rushed out to find out what was happening. He returned almost immediately, crying, 'Sir, there is no more railway!'

'What do you mean?' asked Sir Francis.

'I mean that the train goes no further.'

The General immediately got off the train. Phileas Fogg, in no hurry, followed him. Both spoke to the conductor.

'Where are we?' asked Sir Francis. The conductor told him.

'Do we stop here?'

'We have to. The railway is not finished.'

'What! It is not finished?'

'No! There are still fifty more miles to build between this point and Allahabad, where it starts again.'

'But the papers said that the whole line was now open.'

'Well, the papers were wrong!'

'And you have sold tickets from Bombay to Calcutta!' replied Sir Francis, who was beginning to get rather excited.

'Of course,' replied the conductor, 'but travellers know very well that for this part of the journey they have to find some other kind of transport.'

Sir Francis Cromarty was very angry. Passepartout would have liked to knock the conductor down.

'Sir Francis,' said Mr Fogg simply, 'if you will be kind enough to find out what other kind of transport there is, we will be able to continue our journey.'

'Mr Fogg, this delay will ruin you!'

'No, Sir Francis, I was prepared for it.'

'What! Did you know that the railway — '

'No, of course not, but I knew that something, sooner or later, would delay us. But, don't forget, I have already gained two days. A steamship leaves Calcutta for Hong Kong at noon on the 25th. This is only the 23rd, and we shall arrive at Calcutta in time.'

It was true that the finished part of the railway stopped at this point. The newspapers are like some watches which are always running ahead of time. Most of the passengers knew about this. They left the train and went to the village to get all sorts of vehicles to take them to Allahabad. Mr Fogg and Sir Francis searched through the whole village. They returned to the train without having found anything.　　　　　　　　　　5

Mr Fogg buys an elephant

Passepartout had also been looking around the village, and hesitating a little, he said, 'Sir, I think I have found something which might be suitable.'

'What?'　　　　　　　　　　10

'An elephant belonging to an Indian man living a hundred feet from here.'

'Let us go and see the elephant,' replied Mr Fogg. Five minutes later, Phileas Fogg, Sir Francis Cromarty, and Passepartout arrived at the hut where the man with　15 the elephant lived. Mr Fogg asked him if they could see the elephant.

The man took them outside to where the elephant was. It was a half-tamed animal, which his owner was training to be a fighting elephant, not an elephant to be　20 used for carrying passengers. However, Kiouni — that was the animal's name — could, like all elephants, go quite fast on a long trip, and because they could get nothing else, Phileas Fogg was determined to have him. But when Mr Fogg asked the man if he could use the　25 elephant, he refused.

Mr Fogg continued his request, and offered a very high price for the animal, but nothing could persuade the owner. Then Mr Fogg offered to buy the elephant, and offered the man one thousand pounds. He would　30 still not sell!

Sir Francis put his hand on Mr Fogg's arm and begged him to stop. Phileas Fogg replied that he was

not in the habit of doing anything without a good
reason, and that a bet worth twenty thousand pounds
meant that this elephant was necessary to him, and that
he was prepared to pay more than twenty times his
5 value in order to get him.

Mr Fogg turned back to the owner, whose eyes
seemed to light up at the thought of all that money.
Mr Fogg could see that if the price were high enough,
the man would agree. Phileas Fogg offered him twelve
10 hundred, fifteen hundred, eighteen hundred and
finally two thousand pounds.

At two thousand pounds the owner agreed.

Now all that they needed was to find a guide to take
them to Allahabad. That was a lot easier than obtaining
15 the elephant. A young Indian, with an interesting,
clever face, offered to guide them. He could also drive
the elephant. Mr Fogg accepted him, and said he would
give him a large reward if he were really good. The
elephant was brought out and made ready.

20 Phileas Fogg paid the owner of the elephant in
banknotes taken from his bag. Then Mr Fogg asked Sir
Francis if he would like to go with them to Allahabad.
The General said that he would. It was easy for this
enormous animal to carry one more passenger. All the
25 necessary food was bought. Sir Francis sat on one
side of the elephant's back, and
Mr Fogg sat on the other.
Passepartout sat across the
animal's back between them.
30 The guide sat on the
elephant's neck. They left
the end of the railway
line at nine o'clock and
entered the thick forest
35 that was all around.

4

Passepartout Becomes a Hero

The guide, in order to shorten the journey, left the road. The trip would be shorter by twenty miles if they went through the forest.

Phileas Fogg and Sir Francis Cromarty were very shaken about by the rough movements of the elephant, but they said nothing. Their driver-guide had been told they were in a hurry and for this reason the elephant was made to go as fast as possible.

After two hours' march, the guide stopped the elephant, and gave him an hour's rest. Sir Francis did not complain about the halt. He was very tired. Mr Fogg looked as if he had just got up after a pleasant sleep.

'That man is made of iron!' said the General to himself.

At noon they set off again, moving as fast as they could. The country around them soon began to look very wild. They were going through a part of India that is rarely visited by travellers, and the only Indians that live here are very religious Hindus. The British Government has little control over this part.

Towards late afternoon of the second day, they began to slow down. Allahabad was less than twelve miles away to the north-east. They had avoided all the villages along their way, because the guide thought it safer that not too many people should see them. Up to then there had been no unpleasant meetings, and it seemed as if the journey would be finished without any accidents. Then suddenly the elephant stopped, showing some signs of uneasiness.

It was then four o'clock.

'What is the matter?' asked Sir Francis.

'I do not know, sir,' replied the driver, listening to a strange sound which came through the thick branches of the forest.

A few moments later the sound was clearer. It was like a band. They could hear voices. Passepartout's eyes and ears were wide open. Mr Fogg waited patiently, without saying a word.

The driver jumped down and tied the elephant to a tree. Then he disappeared into the forest. A few minutes later he returned, saying, 'A Hindu group is coming this way. If it is possible we must avoid being seen.'

The guide untied the elephant and led him deeper into the forest. He told the travellers it would be better if they did not get down. He himself was ready to jump up onto the elephant if the Hindus discovered them. But he thought that the religious group would pass by without noticing them, because the thick forest hid them very well.

The sounds of voices and musical instruments got louder. Soon the beginning of the group could be seen, about fifty feet away from Mr Fogg and his companions. Through the branches they could easily see the people in the religious group passing near them.

The funeral

In the first line were the priests. They were surrounded by men, women and children, who seemed to be singing some kind of song for the dead. Some of the men were carrying drums which they beat steadily. Behind them came a carriage with very large wheels. On this was a statue. It had four arms. The body was painted red. Its eyes were dead-looking, the hair was untidy and the tongue was hanging out.

Sir Francis recognized this statue.

'The goddess Kali,' he whispered, 'the goddess of love.'

'Of death, I agree, but of love, never!' replied Passepartout. 'This statue looks like an ugly, dead thing!' 5

Around the statue were a group of old men, jumping about and crying out horribly. Blood ran down their bodies, coming from tiny cuts in their skin.

Behind them a woman was being dragged along. She could hardly stay upright. She was young and 10 beautiful. Her head, her neck, her shoulders, her ears, her arms, her hands and her toes were weighed down with all kinds of jewellery.

Behind this young woman were guards, with swords and guns. They were carrying a kind of bed, and on it 15 lay the dead body of an old man, dressed in rich clothes. Behind him came the musicians.

Sir Francis understood what was happening. He turned to the guide, and said, 'A suttee!'

The woman must die

20

The guide nodded his head and put his fingers to his lips. At last the large group of people disappeared into the forest.

Phileas Fogg had heard the word spoken by Sir Francis, and as soon as the Hindus had disappeared, he asked, 'What is a suttee?'

'A suttee, Mr Fogg,' replied the General, 'is a human sacrifice. The woman that you have just seen will be burnt tomorrow.'

'Oh, how terrible!' cried Passepartout, who could
5 not help crying out.

'And the dead man?' asked Mr Fogg.

'He is her husband,' replied the guide. 'He was a prince in this area.'

'How is it,' asked Phileas Fogg, calmly, 'that these
10 terrible customs still happen in India, and why hasn't the Government been able to stop them?'

'In most of India,' replied the General, 'these sacrifices no longer happen. But the Government has no control in this wild area.'

15 'That poor woman,' whispered Passepartout. 'She will be burnt alive!'

'Yes,' replied the General, 'burnt alive, and if she wasn't, you could not believe how horrible her life would be. Her relatives would feed her only a very little
20 rice. They would cut off all her hair and cover her with dirt. They would all stay away from her and she would die in some corner like a sick dog.'

When the General had finished speaking, the guide said, 'You are right, but the sacrifice which will happen
25 tomorrow is still a terrible thing. That young woman does not want to die.'

'How do you know?'

'Everyone in this area knows,' replied the guide.

'But the poor woman was not fighting against her
30 guards,' said Sir Francis.

'That is because she had been given something to drink which makes her too sleepy to know what is happening.'

'But where are they taking her?'

35 'To a temple two miles from here.'

Fogg plans to rescue the woman

The guide brought the elephant, jumped on his neck and made him kneel down so that the others could get on. But Mr Fogg stopped them. He looked at Sir Francis and said, 'If only we could save this woman!'

'Save the woman, Mr Fogg!' cried the General.

'I still have twelve hours. There is time to save her.'

The idea was bold, full of difficulties and probably impossible. Mr Fogg was going to risk his life, and therefore the success of his plans, but he did not hesitate. He found also that Sir Francis was very willing to help.

As for Passepartout, he was ready for anything and was a good man to have when there was trouble about. His master's idea excited him. He felt that Mr Fogg had a heart after all.

Then there was the guide. Would he be willing to help them?

Sir Francis asked him how he felt.

The guide replied that he would be very pleased to help them save the poor woman.

'I am glad,' replied Mr Fogg.

'However, you must know,' said the guide, 'that, as well as risking our lives, we risk horrible punishment if we are caught.'

'We understand that,' replied Mr Fogg, but he did not seem to want to talk any more about getting caught. Instead he said, 'I think we shall have to wait until night before we can do anything.'

'I think so, too,' replied the guide.

The brave guide then told them about the woman. He said she was the daughter of a rich merchant of Bombay. She had had an English education there. Her name was Aouda. She was very beautiful.

Both Aouda's parents had died and she had been forced to marry the old prince that they had just seen. Three months after her wedding, her husband had died. Knowing what would happen to her, she had run away from her husband's relatives, but she had been caught almost immediately.

They decided that the guide should lead the elephant towards the temple and get as near as possible to it. Half an hour later they stopped among some thick trees. They were five hundred feet from the temple where the young woman was held prisoner. They did not know how they would rescue her. They only knew that whatever they were going to do, they would have to do it that night. When daylight arrived, the woman would be killed.

Mr Fogg and his companions waited. Towards six o'clock in the evening, as it got darker, they decided to examine the outside of the temple. As was usual at these sacrifices, all the guards were drinking strong wine. Perhaps they could pass by them quietly and get inside.

The guide, Mr Fogg, Sir Francis Cromarty and Passepartout moved forward quietly. They crept through the forest for ten minutes, then they arrived at the edge of a small river. On the other side of this, they saw a large pile of wood. That was where the sacrifice would take place in the morning. The body of the dead prince was already placed on top of it.

He would be burnt together with his living wife. One hundred feet away from this was the temple.

'Come!' said the guide in a low voice.

Soon the guide stopped at the edge of the open space in front of them. A few fires around the edge lit up the scene. The ground was covered with groups of sleeping men.

The guards are still awake

Close by, among the trees, the temple could be clearly seen. But to the great disappointment of the guide, the guards of the prince were watching at the doors, and walking up and down with their hands on their swords. Phileas Fogg and Sir Francis knew that they would never be successful in a direct attack on the temple. They stopped and talked in low voices.

'Let us wait,' said the General, 'it is not yet eight o'clock, and it is possible that these guards may still fall asleep.'

Phileas Fogg and his companions stretched themselves out at the foot of a tree and waited. They waited until midnight. The situation did not change. The guards still watched outside. It was clear that they were not going to fall asleep.

After a final conversation, the guide said that he was ready to start. Mr Fogg, Sir Francis, and Passepartout followed him. Without making any noise, they walked carefully to the back of the temple.

No one was guarding the back, and no one saw them as they reached the temple walls. Unfortunately, there were no windows and no doors there.

The guide bent down and showed the others what they should do. They were going to make a hole in the wall! Phileas Fogg and his companions only had their pocket knives with them, but the temple walls were made of a mixture of bricks and wood, so it was not difficult to make a hole. Once the first brick was taken out, the others would be easy to remove.

They started work, making as little noise as possible.

The work was going well, but then they had some bad luck. Some guards appeared at the back of the temple. They stood there, making it quite impossible to continue.

'We will have to leave before we are seen,' whispered the General. They returned carefully to the trees.

Passepartout climbed up into one of the trees and began thinking to himself. He had had an idea earlier and he was now trying to see if he could really make it work.

Anyway, Passepartout could not think of anything else. He slid down the tree he was sitting in, and disappeared into the forest.

The hours were passing, and soon the first light of the morning sun could be seen, although it was still quite dark where Mr Fogg and his companions were.

The guards and some of the other people began to get up and walk around. The doors of the temple were opened. The inside of the temple was lit up and Mr Fogg and Sir Francis could see the young woman who was to be sacrificed. She seemed to have fainted and was being dragged out by the priests.

It took them about two minutes to arrive at the place where the bodies were to be burnt. The woman was stretched out to lie next to her dead husband. Then some of the priests lit the wood on which the two bodies lay.

A dead man comes to life!

Suddenly a loud cry rose up from the watching crowds. People threw themselves on the ground in great fear.

The old prince was not dead! He was seen suddenly rising up, like a ghost. He got on to his feet, picked up

the girl and began
to carry her in his arms
down through the smoke and
flames of the burning pile of wood.

The priests and guards fell to the 5
ground in fear. They were too frightened to look at the
terrible figure that was coming towards them, and
walking past them.

Mr Fogg, Sir Francis and the guide were standing
among the trees, watching. They could not believe their 10
eyes, either. Then the figure of the prince carrying the
girl approached very close to them. 'Quickly! Let us go,
master,' said the prince.

It was Passepartout! He had secretly gone to the
place of sacrifice. He had moved the dead body, put on 15
some of the prince's clothes and waited there on the
unlit fire to rescue the young woman from death!

As quickly as possible, they disappeared into the
woods, and climbed on to the elephant. Soon they
could hear that the guards and priests had recovered 20
from their fear, and had realized that they had been
tricked. They were being followed. Luckily the Indian
guide knew the area well, and after a few frightening
minutes when they thought they might be caught,
Mr Fogg and his companions escaped safely into the 25
jungle.

5

Sent to Prison

Allahabad

The bold plan had succeeded. An hour later, Passepartout was still laughing at his success. As for the young woman, she had no idea what had happened. She had been given something to drink that made her sleep, and she had not yet woken up. The elephant, guided with great skill by the Indian, moved on quickly through the dark jungle. At seven o'clock they stopped.

The General was very worried about the future of the young woman. He told Phileas Fogg that if Mrs Aouda stayed in India, she would almost certainly be forced to return to the people who had just tried to kill her. Phileas Fogg said that he would think over what the General had told him.

Towards ten o'clock, the guide said that they were approaching Allahabad, the town where the railway started again. From there the train would only take a day and a night to reach Calcutta. Phileas Fogg should then be able to arrive in time to catch a steamship which was leaving for Hong Kong at noon on 25th October.

Passepartout was sent out to buy some clothes for Mrs Aouda. Having bought what he considered to be suitable, Passepartout returned to the station where the lady was sitting in the waiting room. She had almost completely recovered. She was a very lovely young woman who spoke beautiful English.

Meanwhile the train was about to leave Allahabad. The Indian guide was waiting. Mr Fogg paid him the amount they had already agreed upon, and no more. This rather surprised Passepartout, who knew that his master owed much to the guide for all his help. The guide had in fact risked his life to help Mr Fogg rescue Mrs Aouda.

Then, there was also the problem of Kiouni, the elephant.

But Phileas Fogg had already decided what to do.

'Guide,' he said to the Indian, 'you have served me well. I wish to give you this elephant.'

The eyes of the guide shone.

'Sir, you are giving me a fortune!' he cried.

A few minutes later, Phileas Fogg, Sir Francis Cromarty, Passepartout, and Mrs Aouda, were seated in a comfortable part of the train which was running at full speed towards Calcutta.

Mrs Aouda recovers

During the journey, the young woman recovered completely. She was surprised to find herself on the train, dressed in European clothes, among travellers that she did not know at all.

Her companions told her gently what had happened. The General told her how kind Mr Fogg had been and how Passepartout had finally rescued her.

Mrs Aouda thanked her new friends over and over again. She could not help the tears that came into her eyes. Then, thinking back to what she had just been through, she shook with fear.

Phileas Fogg could see what she was thinking, and knew that she knew it was not safe for her to stay in India. To make her feel better, he offered to take her to Hong Kong.

Mrs Aouda accepted gratefully. One of her relatives lived in Hong Kong, and she was sure she could live with him.

About half way to Calcutta the train stopped at the
5   station where Sir Francis Cromarty had to get off. The General said goodbye to Phileas Fogg, wishing him all possible success in his journey. Then he said goodbye to Mrs Aouda and Passepartout.

The train moved on and finally, at seven o'clock the
10 next morning, they reached Calcutta.

Phileas Fogg knew that he should arrive in Calcutta on 25th October, twenty-three days after leaving London, and he had arrived on exactly that day. He was neither behind nor ahead of time. Unfortunately, the
15 two days gained between London and Bombay had been lost in this trip across India, but it can be safely said that Phileas Fogg was not at all upset about that.

The steamship for Hong Kong did not leave until noon. When the train arrived in Calcutta, Mr Fogg
20 intended to go straight to the steamship and make sure that Mrs Aouda got safely on board. He did not think it safe for her to spend any unnecessary time in Calcutta.

As they were leaving the railway station, a policeman approached them.

25 'Mr Phileas Fogg?' he asked, looking at Mr Fogg.

'Yes?'

'Is this man your servant?'

'Yes.'

'Will you both be so kind as to come with me,
30 please.'

Taken to court

Mr Fogg made no movement of surprise. Passepartout wanted to argue, but before he could say anything,

Phileas Fogg made a sign that they should obey the policeman.

The policeman took Mr Fogg, Mrs Aouda, and Passepartout to his vehicle. They started off. No one spoke during the twenty minute drive. Finally they stopped in front of an official-looking building. The policeman led his prisoners into a room with no windows, saying to them,

'At half past eight you will appear before Judge Obadiah.'

Then he left and locked the door behind him.

'See! We are prisoners!' cried Passepartout, dropping into a chair. Mrs Aouda turned to Mr Fogg.

'Sir, you must leave me!' she cried. 'It is because of me that this has happened! It is because you rescued me!'

Phileas Fogg only said that that could not be possible. The priests and relatives would never dare to go to the law for help in such a matter as a human sacrifice. He was sure there had been some mistake. Mr Fogg added that he would not leave the young woman, and that he would take her to Hong Kong as planned.

'But the steamship goes at noon!' cried Passepartout.

'Before noon we shall be on board,' was the simple reply from the cool Mr Fogg.

At half past eight the door of the room was opened. The policeman reappeared, and he led the prisoners into the next room. It was a courtroom, and quite a large crowd, of both Europeans and Indians, were already seated there. Mr Fogg, Mrs Aouda, and Passepartout were taken near the front.

The judge, Judge Obadiah, entered almost immediately, followed by the clerk.

'The first case,' the judge said.

'Phileas Fogg?' said the clerk.

'I am here,' replied Mr Fogg.

'Passepartout?'

'Present!' replied Passepartout.

'Good!' said Judge Obadiah. 'For two days, prisoners, you have been looked for on all the trains arriving from Bombay.'

'But what are we accused of?' asked Passepartout impatiently.

'You shall know now,' replied the judge.

At an order from the judge a door was opened and three Indian priests were led into the courtroom.

'Well, well,' whispered Passepartout to himself, 'they are the men who were going to burn our young lady!'

Guilty!

The priest stood up before the judge, and the clerk read in a loud voice the crime that had been commited by Passepartout and Phileas Fogg. They were accused of behaving badly in a holy temple.

'You have heard the crime?' asked the judge, looking at Phileas Fogg.

'Yes, sir,' replied Phileas Fogg, looking at his watch, 'and I confess it is true.'

'Ah! You do?'

'Yes, and I expect these three priests to confess, too, what they were going to do at the temple in the jungle.'

The priests looked at each other. They did not seem to understand what Mr Fogg had said.

'Truly!' cried Passepartout, 'they were going to burn the body of a live woman at that temple!'

The priests looked very surprised, and so did the judge.

'What woman?' he asked. 'Burn whom? In the heart of the city of Bombay?'

'Bombay?' cried Passepartout.

'Certainly. We are not speaking of a temple in the jungle, but of the one in Bombay.'

'And as proof, here are your shoes,' added the clerk, putting a pair on the desk in front of him.

'Oh, yes. Those are my shoes!' cried Passepartout, who was greatly surprised, and spoke without thinking.

What was happening was the work of Detective Fix. He had stayed in Bombay in order to persuade the three priests to go to court. He knew that the Government was very careful to protect their religion. He sent the three priests to Calcutta and made sure they had a warrant for the arrest of Passepartout, for wearing shoes in the temple.

A policeman had watched all the trains arriving from Allahabad. Fix had been puzzled by Mr Fogg's delay, and by the appearance of the woman, Mrs Aouda. But he did not worry about these things too much, for now he could prevent Mr Fogg from continuing his journey until he received the other warrant, from London, for the bank robbery.

The judge had heard Passepartout's thoughtless confession.

'You admit that the shoes are yours?'

'It is true,' said Mr Fogg coldly.

'Since that is so,' continued the judge, 'and since the law protects all the different religions of India, I find Passepartout guilty of a crime against the Hindu religion. The crime is that, on the 20th day of October, he walked into a Hindu temple in Bombay without removing his shoes. I therefore order that the man Passepartout will be put in prison for fifteen days and fined three hundred pounds.'

5   'Three hundred pounds!' cried Passepartout.

'Silence!' called out the clerk.

'And,' added the judge, 'since the master should be responsible for the servant, I order that the man Phileas Fogg be put in prison for eight days and fined one
10 hundred and fifty pounds. Clerk, call the next prisoner!'

Fix, who had been sitting in a corner watching all this, was very satisfied. Phileas Fogg would have to stay in Calcutta for eight days! It would be more than enough time for the warrant to arrive from London.

15   Passepartout had never felt worse. This would ruin his master. He would lose his bet of twenty thousand pounds, and all because, he, Passepartout, had gone into that temple with his shoes on!

Mr Fogg pays bail

20 Phileas Fogg did not look at all upset. He was not even frowning. But at the moment that the clerk was calling the next prisoner, he rose, and said, 'I offer bail.'

'It is your right,' replied the judge.

Fix felt a nasty cold feeling run down his back, but
25 he recovered when he heard what the judge said next, 'Because Mr Phileas Fogg and his servant are both foreigners here, bail will have to be high. One thousand pounds each!'

It would cost Mr Fogg two thousand pounds not to
30 go to prison.

'I will pay it,' said Mr Fogg calmly.

'The money shall be returned to you as soon as the fifteen days have passed and you return to collect it,' said the judge. 'In the meantime, you are free.'

'Come,' said Phileas Fogg to his servant.

'But they should at least return my shoes to me,' cried Passepartout, angrily.

They returned his shoes to him.

Passepartout followed his master and Mrs Aouda out of the courtroom. Fix still hoped that Mr Fogg would not want to lose the sum of two thousand pounds, and that he would wait in Calcutta until the fifteen days were over. But he decided that he had better watch Mr Fogg carefully, just in case he should disappear.

Fix followed Mr Fogg and his companions down to the harbour. Half a mile out to sea the steamship *Rangoon* was waiting, nearly ready to sail. It was eleven o'clock. Mr Fogg had one hour to get on board. He waved to a small boat to take them all out to the *Rangoon*.

Fix, watching all this, felt himself grow angry. 'He is going! Two thousand pounds sacrificed! Ah! But I will follow him to the end of the world, if it is necessary. But the way he is behaving, all that stolen money will soon be finished. Then he will have to stop moving around!'

The detective had good reason for making this remark. The money Mr Fogg had spent on the cost of the tickets, the rewards, the elephant, the bail, and the fines, all added up to more than five thousand pounds. Poor Fix. The reward he hoped to get for recovering the money was growing smaller and smaller all the time.

6

The Journey to Hong Kong

Fix makes his plans

Fix got a cabin on the *Rangoon*, too. He succeeded in getting on board without Passepartout noticing him. He had told the Consul in Calcutta that when the warrant arrived, it must be sent on to Hong Kong.

What would happen in Hong Kong was very important to Detective Fix. Mr Fogg must be caught there, he thought, or he would not be caught at all. This was because Hong Kong was the last place where he could arrest Phileas Fogg. Beyond Hong Kong were Japan, China and America, and a British warrant would be of no use in those countries.

'Either the warrant will be at Hong Kong and I will get my man,' thought Fix during the long hours on the boat, 'or it will not have arrived, and then I must delay his leaving! If I miss him at Hong Kong, people will no longer believe that I am a good detective! Whatever happens, I must succeed. But how shall I do it?'

In the end, Fix decided that he must talk to Passepartout. Fix was sure that Passepartout would help him if he told him that Mr Fogg was a bank robber. But it was a dangerous thing to do. If Passepartout said anything to his master, he would take the necessary action to avoid capture.

Fix decided that he would only use this plan if he could think of nothing better. First of all he would ask the Frenchman a few questions. He knew it was quite easy to get him to talk. Fix stopped trying to hide from Passepartout, and went out to find him.

Fix and Passepartout meet again

'Is this really you, on the *Rangoon*, Mr Passepartout?'

'Mr Fix!' replied Passepartout, much surprised to see the man he had last seen on the *Mongolia*. 'Why! I left you in Bombay, and now I meet you again going to Hong Kong! Are you making the tour of the world, too?'

'No, no,' replied Fix. 'I expect to stay in Hong Kong for a number of days.'

'Ah!' said Passepartout, who still seemed a little puzzled. 'But why haven't I seen you on board before now?'

'Well, I have been rather seasick. How is your master, Phileas Fogg?'

'He is in perfect health and not one day behind on his trip! Ah! Mr Fix, you do not know it, but we have a young lady with us also.'

'A young lady!' replied the detective, who acted exactly as if he did not understand.

But Passepartout soon told him the whole story. Fix nodded with interest and horror. He even seemed surprised when he heard of what happened in Calcutta, though of course he already knew about that part.

After this, Passepartout and the detective met often. But Passepartout was puzzled by meeting Fix on board the same ship that they were on. The man seemed to be following the same route as Mr Fogg. But why?

If Passepartout had thought for a hundred years, he would never have guessed the truth. He would never have imagined that Phileas Fogg was being followed around the world because someone thought he was a bank robber. But Passepartout did think of something. He thought that Fix must be working for Mr Fogg's friends at the Reform Club. He must be following Mr Fogg to prove that this tour of the world was done properly and in the time agreed upon. 'Yes, that is the answer!' he thought, very pleased with himself for having been so clever.

Passepartout decided to say nothing of what he knew to his master. He thought Mr Fogg would be upset at not being trusted by his friends in the Reform Club.

Phileas Fogg needed to be in Hong Kong before 5th November. On that day the steamship that he wanted to take to Japan left Hong Kong. It was going to Yokohama, one of the biggest ports in Japan.

Twenty-four hours behind

During the last few days of the voyage, the weather became very bad. The ship could not go fast because the sea was too rough. The passengers were told that they would arrive in Hong Kong at least twenty hours late.

Mr Fogg did not seem upset about the delay. Mrs Aouda, who talked to him about it, found him as calm as ever.

Fix did not think about these things in the same way. He was very pleased about the bad weather. Any delay meant that Mr Fogg would have to spend more time in Hong Kong trying to find another boat to take him to Japan, or anywhere else he wanted to go. Fix was a little seasick, it is true, but what did that matter?

Passepartout, of course, was very upset, and nothing could make him happy.

Finally the weather got better, and then Passepartout felt better as well. The *Rangoon* was soon going full speed for Hong Kong once more. But all the time lost could not be recovered. They did not reach Hong Kong until the 6th.

When the
passengers landed,
Mr Fogg went to one
of the officials of the
harbour and asked the man
if he knew when a ship would
leave Hong Kong for Yokohama.

'Tomorrow morning,' replied the official.

'Ah,' said Mr Fogg, without showing any
joy or surprise.

Passepartout, who was there, would have
liked to have kissed the official.

'What is the name of the ship?' asked Mr Fogg.

'The *Carnatic*,' replied the official.

'Wasn't she supposed to leave yesterday?'

'Yes, sir, but they had to repair one of her engines,
and it won't be ready until tomorrow.'

'Thank you,' replied Mr Fogg.

It must be made clear how lucky all this was. If the
Carnatic had left on 5th November, Mr Fogg could not
have found another ship to take them to Yokohama
until the following week. It is true that Mr Fogg was
twenty-four hours behind, but this delay was not so
serious because the ship which sailed from Yokohama
to San Francisco always waited for the steamship to
come from Hong Kong. The twenty-four hours lost
could be easily regained during the voyage to San
Francisco, because it was such a long one. It took
twenty-two days to cross the Pacific normally, but a
good, fast ship could often do it in less.

10

15

20

25

30

The *Carnatic* did not leave until five o'clock the next morning, so Mr Fogg found rooms for them in a hotel. He had sixteen hours in Hong Kong to help Mrs Aouda.

Mrs Aouda must go to Europe

5   They soon learnt that Mrs Aouda's uncle no longer lived in Hong Kong. He had made his fortune two years earlier and had gone to live in Europe, in Holland. Phileas Fogg immediately said that Mrs Aouda should go on to Europe with them, and he asked Passepartout
10 to get three cabins on the *Carnatic*.

Passepartout, delighted that the young lady was going on with them, left the hotel immediately. He very quickly found the ship he was looking for, but he also found Detective Fix there.

15 Fix was walking up and down next to the ship looking very unhappy. He had good reason to be upset. No warrant! It was clear that the warrant was coming, but it would only reach him in Hong Kong if he waited there for some days. While Fix was thinking about all
20 this, Passepartout walked up to him.

'Well, Mr Fix, have you decided to come with us as far as America?'

'Yes,' replied Fix between his closed teeth.

'Well, well!' cried Passepartout, shouting with
25 laughter. 'I knew that you could not separate yourself from us.'

They both entered the ticket office to get their cabins. Then the clerk told them that because the repairs had been finished quicker than expected, the
30 *Carnatic* would leave at eight o'clock that evening, and not the next morning.

'Good!' replied Passepartout. 'That will suit my master very well. I will go and tell him.'

At this moment, Fix decided to try to get Passepartout to help him. He decided to tell Passepartout everything. It was the only way, perhaps, that he could keep Phileas Fogg for a few days in Hong Kong.

A friendly drink

5

Leaving the office, Fix offered to buy his companion a drink. Passepartout had the time. He accepted Fix's invitation.

There was a bar nearby. They went in. It had a large room, nicely decorated. At the back there was a kind of 10
bed with a number of people lying on it, asleep.

There were about thirty people grouped around the small tables. Most of them were drinking English beer, and a lot of them were smoking long pipes filled with opium. From time to time, someone would fall asleep. 15
Then, the waiters would pick him up and carry him over to the bed and lay him down next to the others.

Fix and Passepartout realized that the bar they had entered was more than just a drinking house: one could buy opium here as well. Fix ordered two large glasses 20
of a strong wine. The Frenchman drank his happily while Fix watched him. They talked of one thing and another, and especially of Mr Fix's idea of joining the *Carnatic*. The glasses now being empty, Passepartout rose to go and tell his master that the steamship would 25
leave sooner than planned.

Fix stopped him.

'One moment,' he said.

'What do you want, Mr Fix?'

'I have some serious matters to talk to you about.' 30

'Serious matters?' cried Passepartout, emptying the last few drops of wine remaining in the bottom of his glass. 'Very well, we will talk about them tomorrow. I haven't the time today.'

'No, wait,' replied Fix. 'It concerns your master.'

There was something about Fix's voice that made Passepartout sit down again.

'What do you want to say to me?' he asked.

Fix shows his real purpose

Fix ordered some more wine. He placed his hand upon his companion's arm, and speaking very softly, he asked him, 'You have guessed who I am?'

'Of course,' said Passepartout, smiling.

'Then I am going to tell you everything.'

'I think I know everything, my friend. There is twenty thousand pounds to be won or lost.'

'Fifty-five thousand!' replied Fix, taking the Frenchman's hand.

'What!' cried Passepartout. 'Fifty-five thousand pounds! Well, well! All the more reason that I should leave,' he added, rising.

'Fifty-five thousand pounds!' replied Fix, who forced Passepartout to sit down again. He poured some more wine into Passepartout's glass. 'And if I succeed, I get a reward of two thousand pounds. I will give you five hundred if you will help me.'

'Help you!' cried Passepartout, whose eyes were open very wide.

'Yes, help me to keep Mr Fogg in Hong Kong for a few days!'

'What are you saying?' said Passepartout. 'Are you trying to make it impossible for Mr Fogg to do his tour in eighty days? Did the gentlemen at the Reform Club tell you to do this so that they will win? I am ashamed of them.'

'Ah! What do you mean by that?' asked Fix.

'I mean that what you are doing is just like taking Mr Fogg's money away from him.'

'Ah! Exactly! That is just what I plan to do.'

'But that is a terrible thing to do!' cried Passepartout, who was getting very excited after all the wine he had drunk.

Fix is puzzled

'How can gentlemen of the Reform Club do something like this!' cried Passepartout. 'You must know, Mr Fix, that my master is an honest man, and that, when he makes a bet, he intends to win it fairly.'

'But who do you think I am?' asked Fix, looking closely at Passepartout.

'A man sent by the members of the Reform Club, to make sure that my master's journey cannot succeed. At first I thought you were only following, to make sure that he did not cheat. I thought that was bad enough because Mr Fogg is an honest man who would never cheat. I thought it would upset my master, so I took good care not to let him know about you.'

'He knows nothing?' asked Fix quickly.

'Nothing,' answered Passepartout, emptying his glass once more.

The detective hesitated before continuing the conversation. What should he do? Passepartout had clearly got everything wrong, and it made his plan even more difficult. It was clear, though, that the Frenchman was in no way connected with his master's crime.

'Listen,' said Fix, 'listen carefully to me. I am not what you think. I am not working for the members of the Reform Club — '

'Really?' said Passepartout, looking at him unbelievingly.

'I am a police detective, working for the British Government.'

'You — a police detective!'

'Yes, and I will prove it,' replied Fix. 'Here are my papers.'

Passepartout refuses to believe Fix

Passepartout was completely surprised. He was unable to speak.

'Listen,' continued Fix. 'On 29th September the Bank of England was robbed of fifty-five thousand pounds. The police were able to get a description of the man who robbed the bank. That description fits Mr Fogg exactly.'

'Rubbish!' cried Passepartout. 'My master is the most honest man in the world!'

'How do you know?' replied Fix. 'You know nothing about him. You became his servant the day that he left England in a hurry, and for a very odd reason. He took no baggage, but he did take a great deal of money, in banknotes! And you dare to say that he is an honest man?'

'Yes, yes!' repeated poor Passepartout.

'Do you wish, then, to be arrested as his helper?'

Passepartout dropped his head in his hands. The news had surprised him terribly. He did not want to look at the detective. His master, Phileas Fogg, the man who had risked everything to save Mrs Aouda, this brave and kind man, could not be a bank robber! And yet everything seemed to point towards it. Passepartout tried to force back the thoughts that had come into his mind. He would never believe that his master was guilty.

'What do you want me to do?' he asked the detective.

'Well,' replied Fix, 'I have followed Mr Fogg as far as Hong Kong, but I have not yet received the warrant of arrest, which I have asked for, from London. You must help me, then, to keep him here — '

'I! Help you!'

'And I will share with you the reward of two thousand pounds.'

'Never!' replied Passepartout, who wanted to rise, but fell back. He felt very weak. 'Mr Fix,' he said unclearly, 'even if my master is the robber that you are looking for, which I don't believe, I am still his servant. I have seen that he is kind and generous. I could never do to him what you ask. Never!

'You refuse?'

'I refuse.'

'Then let us forget that I ever said anything,' replied Fix, 'and let's have another drink.'

'All right, let's have another drink!'

Passepartout knew he was becoming very drunk. Fix, knowing that he must at all costs keep Passepartout away from his master, wanted to make sure that he couldn't move. On the table there were a few pipes filled with opium. Fix slipped one into Passepartout's hand. Passepartout took it without thinking about what he was doing. He lit it and took in a few deep breaths. Then he fell over. He was not strong enough to take both the wine and the opium.

'At least,' said Fix, seeing that Passepartout could not damage his plans that night, 'Mr Fogg will not be told that the *Carnatic* is leaving early.'

7
Master and Servant Meet Again

The *Carnatic* has left

Mr Fogg had no idea of what was happening to his servant. He did not worry that night when he did not see Passepartout before he went to bed. It was not part of Mr Fogg's character to worry.

The next morning, Passepartout did not appear when his master called for him, but Mr Fogg still did not seem to worry. When he and Mrs Aouda were both ready, they went down to the harbour. It was clear that Mr Fogg expected to find both the *Carnatic* and his servant there. Neither could be seen, but not a sign of disappointment appeared on his face.

At this moment a person who had been watching him closely, came up to him. It was Detective Fix, who turned to him and said, 'Are you, like myself, sir, one of the passengers of the *Rangoon*, who arrived yesterday?'

'I am, sir,' replied Mr Fogg.

'Pardon me, but I thought I would find your servant here.'

'Do you know where he is, sir?' asked Mrs Aouda quickly.

'What!' replied Fix, pretending to be surprised. 'Isn't he with you?'

'No,' replied Mrs Aouda. 'He has not returned since yesterday. Do you think he could have gone without us on the *Carnatic*?'

'Without you, madam?' replied Fix. 'But, excuse my question, did you expect to leave by that steamship?'

'Yes, sir.'

'I did too, madam, and am very disappointed. The *Carnatic* left twelve hours sooner than expected without warning anyone. Now we must wait a week for another ship.' 5

Fix felt very happy. Mr Fogg would have to spend a week in Hong Kong now! The warrant would arrive, and he could arrest this bank robber.

'But there are other ships, I am sure, in the port of Hong Kong,' said Fogg. 10

Mr Fogg, offering his arm to Mrs Aouda, turned towards the harbour to search for a ship that would take him where he wanted to go.

Fix, unable to think of anything else to do, followed.

Phileas Fogg searched for three hours, but found 15 nothing. Fix began to hope again.

Mr Fogg finds a boat

But Mr Fogg was not worried. Suddenly a sailor came up to him.

'You are looking for a boat, sir?' 20

'You have one ready to sail?' asked Mr Fogg.

'Yes, sir.'

'She goes fast?'

'Yes, sir. Will you look at her?'

'Yes.' 25

'I am sure you will be pleased with her, sir. Where do you want to sail to?'

'I wish to go to Yokohama.'

The sailor stood there with his eyes wide open.

'You are joking, sir?' he said. 30

'No, I have missed the *Carnatic*, and I must be in Yokohama on the 14th at the latest, to take the steamship for San Francisco.'

'I am sorry,' said the sailor, 'but it is impossible.'

'I will offer you one hundred pounds a day, and a reward of two hundred pounds if I arrive in time.'

The sailor looked out to sea; it was clearly difficult for him to decide what to do.

'Well?' asked Mr Fogg.

'Well, sir,' replied the sailor, 'I cannot take you to Yokohama. It is too far and too dangerous, and we will never get there on time.'

Fix took a good long breath.

'But,' added the sailor, 'there might perhaps be another way to do it.'

Fix stopped breathing.

'How?' asked Phileas Fogg.

'By going to Shanghai, which is much nearer to Hong Kong.'

'I have to go to Yokohama,' replied Phileas Fogg, 'to catch the steamship that leaves from there for San Francisco. There is no reason to go to Shanghai.'

'But there is,' replied the sailor. 'The San Francisco steamship does not start from Yokohama; she starts from Shanghai, and stops at Yokohama later.'

'And when does the steamship leave Shanghai?'

'On the 11th, at seven o'clock in the evening. That means that we have four days to get to Shanghai. If the sea is calm and the wind keeps to the south-east, we should be able to do it. But you must be ready to sail within an hour.'

'It is agreed. You are the captain of the boat?'

'Yes, sir. I am John Bunsby, captain of the *Tankadere*.'

'Do you need some money now?'

'It would be helpful, sir, to buy some necessary articles.'

'Here are two hundred pounds,' said Mr Fogg. Then, turning to Fix, he said, 'If you wish to —'

'Sir,' answered Fix quickly, 'I was going to ask this of you.'

'Well, in half an hour we will be on board.'

'But what about Passepartout?' cried Mrs Aouda, looking very worried.

'I am going to do all I can to find him,' replied Phileas Fogg. And he went to the police and the French Consul, where he left both a description of his servant, and some money for him, if he was found.

At three o'clock the *Tankadere* set sail with its three passengers. Mr Fogg and Mrs Aouda took one long last look at the harbour, hoping to see Passepartout.

Fix was worried about Passepartout, too. He didn't know what he would say if Passepartout appeared and told his master everything he knew about the detective.

Phileas Fogg thought it was just possible that Passepartout might be on the *Carnatic* alone. He might not have understood his master's orders, and decided to wait on board for him and Mrs Aouda instead of going back to the hotel. Mrs Aouda agreed that this might be possible, and they both hoped that they would find Passepartout safe in Yokohama.

Will they miss the ship?

On the morning of the 11th, Captain Bunsby told them that they were only one hundred miles from Shanghai.

One hundred miles, and only one day left! If Mr Fogg did not arrive that evening he would miss the steamship for Yokohama and America.

By noon they were only forty-five miles away. They had six hours to get to Shanghai.

By six o'clock there were only ten miles left.

At seven o'clock there were three. The captain swore. It was clear that the reward of two hundred pounds was going to slip through his fingers. He looked at Mr Fogg. The man's face told him nothing, and yet Phileas Fogg's whole future was in question at that moment.

At that moment too, a long, black line appeared in the distance. It was the American steamship that Fogg had hoped to catch, leaving Shanghai for San Francisco at the normal time — seven o'clock.

'Signal her,' said Phileas Fogg simply.

The *Tankadere* had a small deck gun. It was used to make signals in bad weather. The gun was loaded, but at the moment when the captain was about to fire, Mr Fogg said, 'Raise your flag first.'

The flag was raised half way. This was a distress signal, and they hoped that the American steamship, seeing it, would come to help them.

'Fire!' said Mr Fogg.

The noise of the gun sounded through the air.

These signals were noticed by the American ship, and it was not long before Captain Bunsby's three

passengers were being helped on board the *General Grant*, as the American steamship was called.

Phileas Fogg paid Captain Bunsby exactly the amount agreed upon.

In Yokohama

On the morning of the 14th, the *General Grant* steamed into Yokohama. Mr Fogg went immediately to where he saw the *Carnatic* was, and asked about his servant. There he learnt, to the great joy of Mrs Aouda, that Passepartout had indeed sailed on the *Carnatic* to Yokohama. He had just gone ashore, but was expected back at any minute.

Just then, the familiar form of Passepartout appeared on the ship. His face lit up with joy as he saw them.

'Ah! My master! My master!' cried Passepartout. Then his face fell. He suddenly realized that his master, whom he was so pleased and relieved to see, was probably very angry with him. Quickly, and in a trembling voice he told something of what had happened to him. He told his master and Mrs Aouda how he had got very drunk. He did not mention Fix, as he thought it was not yet time to tell his master what had passed between himself and the detective. He told them how he had struggled against the effects of the wine he had drunk. Somehow he knew that he had to tell his master about the *Carnatic* leaving early. He finally got out of the bar, hardly able to stand upright, crying, 'The *Carnatic*!

The ship was there at the side of the harbour. Passepartout had only a few steps to go. He rushed onto the ship and then fell onto the deck. Some of the sailors, used to this sort of thing, lifted him up and put him in his cabin, and soon after that the *Carnatic* left the port of Hong Kong. When Passepartout woke up the next morning, the ship was one hundred and fifty miles from Hong Kong. It was only then that he realized what had happened and learnt that his master and Mrs Aouda were not on board. He felt full of guilt because he knew that it was his fault that they had not caught the steamship. Mr Fogg would be ruined, and all because of the stupidity of his servant.

At this point Passepartout halted in his story. His honest, simple face showed that he could not understand how indeed his master and Mrs Aouda were there in Yokohama in time to catch the steamship to San Francisco.

Mrs Aouda soon told him what had happened to them since they had last met, and Passepartout heard, without letting anyone know what he was thinking, that a person called Fix had travelled with them.

Mr Fogg had listened coldly to both his servant's story and Mrs Aouda's. Without saying anything, he opened his purse and gave Passepartout some money to pay for cabins for the three of them on the *General Grant*.

Fix follows them to San Francisco

That evening the *General Grant* set sail from Yokohama for San Francisco. On board were Mr Fogg, Mrs Aouda and Passepartout. The ship was expected to make the journey in twenty-one days. Mr Fogg expected to land at San Francisco on 2nd December. He would then be in New York on the 11th, and in London on the 20th, thus gaining some hours on the final date of the 21st of December.

Now, where was Fix at this moment?

He was actually on board the *General Grant*.

In fact, on arriving in Yokohama, the detective had left Mr Fogg and gone straight to the British Consul.

There he finally found the warrant of arrest, which, after following him from Bombay, was already forty days old! It had arrived in Yokohama the day before. In fact it had arrived on the *Carnatic*! The detective's disappointment can be imagined. The warrant was useless! Mr Fogg was no longer on British soil.

'Well,' said Fix to himself, after the first moment of anger, 'my warrant is no good here, but it will be good in England. This robber appears to want to go on to England, so I will follow him there!' His decision taken, he immediately bought a ticket to America and went on board the *General Grant*.

Fix was on the *General Grant* when Mr Fogg and Mrs Aouda returned with Passepartout. Fix immediately hid himself in his cabin. He had no wish to explain himself — that could damage all his plans. He thought that he would be able to hide himself from Passepartout during the voyage.

Of course, on such a long voyage, he could not hope to succeed. One day Detective Fix and Passepartout found themselves face to face. Without saying a word, Passepartout jumped at Fix and held him by the throat. He then started to give the detective a heavy beating.

Passepartout felt much better when he had finished.

Fix stood up very slowly, and looking at Passepartout, said, 'Have you finished?' 'Yes, for the moment.'

'Then I want to speak to you.'

'But I —'

'It is for the good of your master.'

Passepartout silently followed the detective to the forward part of the ship.

'You have beaten me,' said Fix. 'I expected it. Now, listen to me. Until now I have been trying to stop Mr Fogg from succeeding in travelling fast, but now I want to help him.'

'At last!' cried Passepartout. 'You believe him to be an honest man.'

'No,' replied Fix coldly. 'I still believe that he is the bank robber. I will tell you why my behaviour has changed. As long as Mr Fogg was travelling through British lands, I wanted to keep him there so that my warrant for arrest had time to reach me. I did everything I could for that. I persuaded the priests in Bombay to complain about him to the courts. I made you drunk in Hong Kong and separated you from your master and made him miss the Yokohama steamship. Now Mr Fogg seems to be returning to England, and it is in my interest to see that he gets there as quickly as possible.'

Passepartout listened to Fix very carefully. He believed Fix when he said that he now wanted to help his master to travel quickly.

'Very well, then,' Passepartout said at last. 'We will join together to help Mr Fogg get to England quickly. But, be careful! If you do anything to cause him to go slowly, I will break your neck!'

'Agreed,' said the detective quietly.

For some reason, on this trip Mr Fogg was unlucky. He had hoped to arrive in San Francisco on 2nd December and, so be ahead of his timetable once again. Unfortunately the *General Grant* did not arrive until the 3rd. Mr Fogg had neither lost nor gained a single day.

8

The Journey across America

Attacked by Red Indians

New York and San Francisco were joined by railway. In fact, there were 3,786 miles of railway between the two cities. Part of the country the railway passed through was still controlled by the Red Indians. The US army did its best to make it safe for farmers and travellers.

From what he knew of the train, and his timetable, Phileas Fogg hoped that this journey would be over in seven days so that he would be able to catch the Liverpool steamship, on the 11th, from New York.

After three days and three nights, the train had gone 1,382 miles from San Francisco. Four days and four nights more ought to be enough to reach New York. Phileas Fogg was then still on time.

Mrs Aouda had persuaded Mr Fogg to play his favourite game, whist, and she, Mr Fogg, Mr Fix and one other passenger were happily playing, when suddenly terrible cries and the sound of shooting were heard. The train was being attacked by a group of Indians.

It was not the first attempt of these daring fighters to stop a train. They had guns and horses and they raced along beside the moving train, shooting at the passengers and climbing on board. Most of the passengers, being Americans, carried their own guns, and those that did not were quickly given them by the train guard. Soon a real gun fight was going on between the passengers and the Indians.

At first the Indians rushed to try and capture the engine, and the engineer and his helper were soon killed. An Indian chief tried to stop the train, but did not know how to do it. Instead of slowing the train down, he only made it go faster and faster.

At the same time, the Indians entered the passenger carriages. They ran over the roofs, they forced the doors open and fought hand to hand with the passengers. The baggage car was opened and robbed. Cries and shots went on and on. But the passengers fought bravely, and still the train sped forward, going at about one hundred miles an hour.

From the beginning of the attack Mrs Aouda had joined in. With a gun in her hand, she fired through the window near her whenever she saw an Indian.

Several passengers, very badly wounded, lay upon the seats.

Something had to be done. The attack had already lasted for ten minutes, and the Indians would certainly win if the train was not stopped. Fort Kearney station was only two miles away. There was an army camp there, but once that was passed, the train could expect no help from anyone.

The train guard was fighting next to Mr Fogg. There was a shot, and the guard fell. He had been badly wounded. As he fell, he cried, 'We are lost if the train does not stop within five minutes!'

'It shall be stopped!' said Phileas Fogg calmly. 'I will make sure.' Mr Fogg was about to rush out of the car.

'Stay here sir, with Mrs Aouda,' Passepartout cried out to him. 'I will do it.'

Passepartout stops the train

Phileas Fogg had no time to stop the brave young man, who, opening a door without being seen by the Indians,

got out of the carriage and succeeded in slipping underneath it. While the struggle continued, and while people were shooting at each other above his head, Passepartout slowly made his way to the front of the train. At last, with great skill, he   5
reached the front. He
had not been seen.

There, hanging between the baggage car and the engine, he pulled out the huge iron bar that   10 held the two together, and the train, now free of the engine, began to slow down. It finally stopped less than one hundred feet from Fort Kearney station.

The soldiers, who had heard the firing, ran to the train. The Indians did not wait for them. They knew   15 they could not win against the soldiers.

When the passengers counted each other on the platform of the station, they noticed that several were missing and among them, the brave Frenchman. Had they been killed in the fight? Were they prisoners of the Indians? No one knew.

Many passengers were wounded, but the army doctor said that they would all recover. Mrs Aouda was safe. Phileas Fogg, who had fought very bravely indeed, didn't even have a scratch. Fix was wounded in the arm, but it was not a serious wound. But Passepartout was missing.

Meanwhile all the passengers had left the train. Mr Fogg, with folded arms, stood quite still. He had a serious decision to make. Mrs Aouda, near him, looked at him without saying a word. He understood her look. If his servant was a prisoner, shouldn't he risk everything to rescue him from the Indians?

'I shall find him, dead or alive,' he said simply to Mrs Aouda.

'Ah! Mr Fogg — Mr Fogg!' cried the young woman, taking her companion's hands and covering them with tears.

'Alive!' added Mr Fogg, 'if we do not lose a minute!'

With this decision Phileas Fogg sacrificed himself completely. He had just spoken words that would ruin him. A single day's delay would make him miss the steamship from New York. His bet would be lost. But he thought, 'It is my duty!' and he did not hesitate.

The captain commanding Fort Kearney was there. His soldiers, about one hundred men, were waiting nearby.

'Sir,' said Mr Fogg to the captain, 'three passengers have gone.'

'Killed?' asked the captain.

'Killed or taken prisoner,' replied Mr Fogg. 'And I must know which. Will you go after the Indians?'

The captain quickly chose thirty men to go with him and Phileas Fogg. Fix stepped forward and asked if he could go as well.

'You must do as you please,' replied Phileas Fogg. 'But if you wish to help me, you will stay with Mrs Aouda. In case anything happens to me — '

Fogg and the soldiers set off

The detective's face went pale. He did not want to separate himself from the man he had followed for so long. To let him go after the Indians like this! Fix looked closely at the gentleman, and whatever he thought, or believed that Mr Fogg had done in the past, he dropped his eyes before the quiet, clear, honest look that he saw in Mr Fogg's eyes.

'I will stay,' he said.

Just before starting, Mr Fogg promised the soldiers five thousand dollars if they could save the prisoners.

The brave men set out. Mrs Aouda and Fix watched them go.

To Mrs Aouda, Mr Fogg was a hero. He was prepared to sacrifice his fortune and his life, from a sense of duty.

At two o'clock the engine was brought back. It had been found on the railway track about twenty miles beyond the station. Most of the travellers were very pleased to see the engine return. It meant that they could continue their journey.

As the engine arrived, Mrs Aouda came out of the station and asked the train official if the train was going to start at once.

'This very moment, madam.'

'But the prisoners — our companions — '

'I cannot delay the trip any more,' replied the official. 'We are already three hours behind time.'

'And when will the next train be coming from San Francisco?'

'Tomorrow evening, madam.'

'Tomorrow evening! But it will be too late. We must wait — '

'Impossible,' replied the official. 'If you are going, get aboard now.'

'I will not,' replied the young woman.

Fix heard this conversation. A few minutes before he had quite decided that he would go with this train. But now, hearing Mrs Aouda, he decided to stay. Slowly the train started, gathered speed, and soon it disappeared into the distance.

Evening came. Still the rescue party had not returned. Where was it at this moment? Had it been able to find the Indians? Throughout the night nothing moved near the station. It only snowed and snowed, sometimes a lot, sometimes a little.

Dawn came, and still there was no movement.

Passepartout is safe

Then at seven o'clock, a party of men was seen returning to the fort. Phileas Fogg rode at its head, and near him Passepartout and the two other passengers could be seen.

There had been a fight with the Indians about ten miles south of the fort. The Indians fought bravely, but they never had a chance of winning. Passepartout and the others were rescued. The rescuers and the rescued were greeted with cries of joy, and Phileas Fogg divided among the soldiers the reward he had promised them.

'I am certainly costing my master a lot of money,' Passepartout thought to himself.

Fix looked at Mr Fogg. It was impossible to know what he was thinking. The man he believed to be a thief always behaved like a gentleman and a hero.

Passepartout looked around for the train. He thought it would be waiting for them so that they could continue their journey and be able to regain the lost time.

'The train, the train!' he cried.

'Gone,' replied Fix.

'And when will the next train pass?' asked Fogg.

'Not until this evening.'

'Ah!' replied the gentleman simply. He was now twenty hours behind time. Passepartout was very upset. He had certainly ruined his master!

At this moment the detective went up to Mr Fogg. 'I have an idea,' he said. 'You are in a hurry, aren't you?'

'Yes,' said Mr Fogg seriously, 'I am.'

'If your journey hadn't been interrupted you would have arrived in New York on the morning of the 11th.'

'Yes, twelve hours before the Liverpool steamship leaves.'

'Well, now you are twenty hours behind time. The difference between twenty and twelve is eight. Eight hours must be regained. Do you wish to try it?'

'On foot?' asked Mr Fogg.

A sledge with sails

'No,' replied Fix, 'on a sledge with sails. A man who lives here has made such a vehicle, and he says we may use it.'

Mr Fogg went to look at the vehicle. It looked like a boat with a sail and long pieces of wood, called 'runners' underneath. It had six seats.

In a few moments Mr Fogg had bought it, and at eight o'clock the sledge was ready. The sails were raised. The sledge sped across the snow at a speed of about forty miles an hour. It was two hundred miles to

Omaha, but
the land was clear
and flat all the way. It
should take them about
5   five hours. They could then
catch another train on to New York. Instead of arriving
in the morning, they would arrive there in the evening,
but it would be before the Liverpool ship left.

     Everything went well. They arrived safely at Omaha
10   and caught a train to New York almost at once. The next
day, the 10th, at four o'clock in the afternoon, their
train stopped in Chicago to collect more passengers.
There were still nine hundred miles between
themselves and New York.

15   At thirty-five minutes past nine on the evening of
the 11th, the train entered the great New York station.
It was right next to the harbour where the steamships
left for Europe.

     The *China*, going to Liverpool, had left thirty-five
20   minutes before.

9

Mr Fogg Becomes a Sea Captain

Mr Fogg looks for a ship

The *China* seemed to have carried away with her Phileas Fogg's last hope.

In fact none of the other steamships in New York harbour were going to England that day. Mr Fogg checked in his general guidebook which contained all the daily movements of passenger ships throughout the world. There was nothing.

Passepartout was very upset. It almost killed him to know that they had missed the steamship by only thirty-five minutes. It was his fault too! And when he went over in his mind all the things that had happened on the journey because of him, and the money that he had cost his master, he wanted to die. He could not help thinking of the huge bet, the wasted money, the useless journey. Mr Fogg would be ruined, and it was all his fault.

Mr Fogg did not blame him at all. He only said, 'We will try to do something tomorrow. Now, let us find a hotel for the night.'

Mr Fogg slept very well, but Mrs Aouda, Passepartout and Fix, who was still with them, could hardly sleep at all because they were so worried.

The next day was 12th December. From the 12th, at seven in the morning, to the 21st, at nine o'clock in the evening, there remained nine days and fourteen hours. If, then, Phileas Fogg had left the night before in the *China*, one of the best ships working between New York and Liverpool, he would have arrived at Liverpool, and then London, in time!

The following morning Mr Fogg left the hotel alone. He told his servant to wait for him and to make sure that Mrs Aouda was ready so that she could leave quickly if necessary.

Mr Fogg went down to the harbour. Several ships were preparing to go to sea. Of course in this huge port there are always hundreds of ships coming and going every day. But most of them were sailing ships, and they would not suit Fogg. At last he saw a steamship that was preparing to leave.

An unfriendly captain

Phileas Fogg went out to her in a small boat at once. He climbed on board. She was called the *Henrietta*. Her upper parts were of wood and her lower part, the hull, was made of iron.

The captain of the *Henrietta* was on board. The captain was an American man of about fifty. He was never very friendly towards other people.

'Are you the captain?' asked Mr Fogg.

'I am.'

'I am Phileas Fogg of London.'

'And I am Andrew Speedy.'

'You are going to start?'

'In an hour.'

'You are going to — ?'

'Bordeaux.'

'And your cargo?'

'Nothing.'

'You have passengers?'

'I never carry passengers. This is a cargo ship.'

'Your ship goes fast?'

'Between eleven and twelve knots.'

'Would you like to take me and three other people to Liverpool?'

'To Liverpool? Why not to China?'

'I said Liverpool.'

'No! I am setting out for Bordeaux and I shall go to Bordeaux.'

'It doesn't matter what the price is.'

'I don't care about the money!'

The captain's voice showed that he was serious.

'But the owners of the *Henrietta* — ' replied Phileas Fogg.

'I am the owner of the *Henrietta*,' replied the captain.

'I will buy it from you.'

Phileas Fogg made this offer calmly. But the situation was serious.

Until now, Mr Fogg's money had always worked. Not this time. The captain was not interested in selling his ship.

But somehow a ship had to be found.

Phileas Fogg seemed to have an idea, for he said to the captain, 'Well, will you take me to Bordeaux?'

'No, not even if you paid me two hundred dollars.'

'I offer you two thousand.'

'For each person?'

'For each person.'

'And there are four of you?'

'Four.'

Captain Speedy scratched his head. He could make eight thousand dollars and still go to Bordeaux. It was well worth it, even though he didn't like passengers. Besides, at two thousand dollars each, they weren't passengers, they were valuable cargo.

'I leave at nine o'clock,' said Captain Speedy simply.

'At nine o'clock we will be on board!' replied Mr Fogg.

It was already half past eight, but Mr Fogg remained calm and quiet.

He went back to the hotel and told his companions that he had found a ship. He kindly offered Fix a cabin, knowing that he wanted to go as well.

By nine o'clock they were all on board and the 5 *Henrietta* was ready to go.

When Passepartout learnt what this last journey would cost, he almost fainted.

As for detective Fix, he said to himself that the Bank of England would find that most of the fifty-five 10 thousand pounds were spent. Mr Fogg had already spent more than seven thousand pounds!

Mr Fogg takes control

At noon the next day, 13th December, someone went up onto the main deck to take command of the ship. Was it 15 Captain Speedy? Not at all! It was Phileas Fogg. Captain Speedy had been carefully locked up in his cabin, and he was very angry indeed.

What had happened was very simple. Phileas Fogg wanted to go 20 to Liverpool. The captain would not take him there. Then Phileas Fogg agreed to go to Bordeaux, and during the thirty hours that he was 25 on board, he had used his banknotes well. None of the sailors liked

Captain Speedy anyway, for he was a hard man, so for a good reward they were quite ready to have Mr Fogg for their captain.

And this is why Phileas Fogg commanded in the place of Captain Speedy, why the captain was locked up in his cabin, and why, finally, the *Henrietta* was now heading for Liverpool. It was very clear, seeing Mr Fogg commanding the ship, that he had been a sailor once.

Mrs Aouda was rather uneasy, though she said nothing. Fix was really surprised at first. Passepartout found it simply splendid. Fix did not understand what was happening at all. The way Mr Fogg had taken over the ship completely puzzled him. Fix was sure that the ship would not go to Liverpool. He decided in the end, that Mr Fogg must have decided to become a pirate. After all, a sea robber was not so different from a bank robber.

The 16th December was the seventy-fifth day that had passed since leaving London. The *Henrietta* had not yet been seriously delayed, although bad weather had forced her to go more slowly than her passengers liked. Half of the voyage had been completed, and the worst part was over. In summer, success would have been certain. In winter, they were at the mercy of the bad weather.

Now, on this day, the engineer went up on deck, met Mr Fogg, and talked very seriously with him.

Without knowing why, Passepartout felt uneasy. He could only hear a little of what was said. 'You are certain of what you say?' he heard his master ask.

'I am certain, sir,' replied the engineer.

'I will think about what to do,' said Mr Fogg calmly.

Passepartout was not nearly so calm. He suddenly realized what they had been talking about. Coal! They were running out of coal!

Then, meeting Fix, he could not help telling him what he had learnt. And now, what was Phileas Fogg going to do? It was difficult to guess. But it seemed that he had thought of something, for that evening he sent
5   for the engineer and said to him, 'Keep the fires going and continue on your way to Liverpool until all the coal is gone.'

Mr Fogg plans to burn the ship

Two days later, on the 18th, the coal was almost gone.
10   All Mr Fogg did was to order Passepartout to go and fetch Captain Speedy.

Captain Speedy soon appeared, looking very angry.

'Where are we?' were the first words he spoke. His face was purple with anger.

15   'Seven hundred and seventy miles from Liverpool,' replied Mr Fogg calmly.

'Pirate!' cried Andrew Speedy.

Mr Fogg took no notice. 'I have sent for you, sir,' he said, 'to ask you to sell me your ship.'

20   'No! By all the devils, no!'

'I shall have to burn her.'

'Burn my ship!'

'At least the upper part, for we have no more coal.'

'Burn my ship!' cried Captain Speedy. He seemed to
25   have difficulty breathing. 'A ship that is worth fifty thousand dollars!'

'Here are sixty thousand!' replied Phileas Fogg, offering him the banknotes.

This produced a powerful effect on Captain Speedy.
30   His ship was twenty years old. It might be quite a bargain.

'And you will leave me the iron hull?' he asked in a more friendly voice.

'The iron hull and the engine, sir. Is it a bargain?'
'It is.'

And Andrew Speedy took the pile of banknotes, counted them and put them in his pocket.

During all this, Passepartout was watching and listening. He had gone as white as a sheet. As for Fix, he nearly fainted. Nearly twenty thousand pounds spent, and yet this Fogg was going to let the captain keep the hull and the engine. That was nearly the whole value of the ship! It is true that the amount stolen from the Bank of England was fifty-five thousand pounds, but still! Mr Fogg turned to Captain Speedy. 'Sir, don't let this surprise you. If I am not in London on the 21st of December, at nine o'clock in the evening, I will lose twenty thousand pounds.'

'Well,' he said, 'well, Captain Fogg, there is something of the American in you!'

That was high praise indeed, from Captain Speedy.

The upper part of the ship now belonged to Phileas Fogg. He at once gave orders that all the wood should be used to keep the fires going.

On the 21st of December, at twenty minutes before noon, Phileas Fogg finally landed at Liverpool. There was nothing left of the *Henrietta* except her hull and the engine.

Phileas Fogg was only six hours from London. But at this moment Fix came up to him, put his hand on his shoulder, and, showing his warrant, said, 'You are really Phileas Fogg?'

'Yes, I am.'

'Then I arrest you in the name of the Queen!'

10
What Finally Happens

Five minutes too late!

Phileas Fogg was shut up in Liverpool prison, and was to spend the night there, waiting to be taken to London. Now he really was ruined, and at the very
5 moment when he thought success was possible. He had arrived in Liverpool at twenty minutes to twelve on Saturday 21st December. He had until nine o'clock that evening to reach the Reform Club. He had nine hours and twenty minutes and he needed only six to reach
10 London.

He heard the prison clock strike one. If only he was free. He still had time to catch the fast train to London, and he could still arrive in London and at the Reform Club before nine o'clock.

15 At thirty-three minutes past two o'clock, a noise sounded outside. The voices of Passepartout and Fix could be heard.

Phileas Fogg looked happier for a moment.

The door opened, and he saw Mrs Aouda,
20 Passepartout and Fix rushing towards him.

Fix was out of breath, his hair untidy, and he could not speak.

'Sir,' he cried, 'pardon — an unlucky mistake — the robber was arrested three days ago — you — are —
25 free — !'

Phileas Fogg was free! He went to the detective, looked at him carefully, and then made the only hurried movement that he had ever made in his life. He threw back his arm and hit the detective.

'Well done!'
cried Passepartout.

Fix, lying on the floor,
did not say anything. He knew he
deserved what had happened. Then
Mr Fogg, Mrs Aouda and Passepartout left the prison as
quickly as possible. They went straight to the railway
station.

Phileas Fogg asked if there was a fast train ready to
start for London. It was forty minutes past two. The fast
train had left thirty-five minutes before. Phileas Fogg
ordered a special train.

Finally, at three o'clock their special train was ready
to leave for London. The engineer was promised a large
reward if he could get them to London in time.

They arrived at five past nine.

Phileas Fogg, after having completed the tour of the
world, arrived five minutes behind time!

He had lost his bet.

Fogg talks to Mrs Aouda

The next day the house at Saville Row was very quiet.
The doors and windows were all closed.

Phileas Fogg was ruined. And all because of Detective Fix. After travelling steadily during this long journey, avoiding a thousand difficulties and bravely meeting a thousand dangers, and still finding time to do
5 some good on his way, he had failed. It was terrible! He had only a very little of the money he had taken with him for his journey. His fortune was lost. The only money that was left was the twenty thousand pounds in the Baring Brothers Bank, and now he owed that to his
10 friends at the Reform Club.

Mrs Aouda was very upset. She was sure that Mr Fogg would try to kill himself. It was the only honourable thing to do, for an English gentleman.

The clock struck half past eleven. For the first time
15 since he lived there, Phileas Fogg did not go to his Club.

He had already made sure, before he left the country, that his friends at the Reform Club could get the money from his bank without him being there.

At about half past seven in the evening, Mr Fogg sent
20 for Mrs Aouda. A few minutes later he and she were alone in his study.

Phileas Fogg took a chair and sat down near the fire, opposite Mrs Aouda. She could not tell what he was thinking. He was quite calm. He remained without
25 speaking for five minutes. Then, raising his eyes to Mrs Aouda, he said, 'Madam, will you forgive me for bringing you to England?'

'Why?' replied Mrs Aouda, her heart beating fast.

'Please let me finish,' continued Mr Fogg. 'When I
30 took you away from that country which had become dangerous for you, I was rich. I meant to let you have part of my fortune. Your life would then be happy and free. Now, I am ruined.'

'I know that, Mr Fogg,' replied the young woman.
35 'And now I must ask you to forgive me. I followed you

around the world and probably helped to slow you down and delay you. I must have helped to ruin you.'

'Madam, you could not stay in India. You had to leave.'

'So, Mr Fogg,' replied Mrs Aouda, 'you saved me from a terrible death, but you do not have to give me money as well. To save my life was enough.'

'No, madam, it is not as I wish it. But now events have turned against me. However, I have a little left and I hope that you will allow me to give it to you.'

'But, Mr Fogg, what about you?' asked Mrs Aouda.

'I, madam,' replied the gentleman coldly, 'I do not need anything.'

'But what will you do?'

'What I ought to do,' replied Mr Fogg.

'Anyway,' said Mrs Aouda, 'you must have friends who will help you?'

'I have no close friends. The people I know at the Reform Club are partners for whist only.'

'Your relatives — '

'I have no relatives now.'

'I am sorry, then, Mr Fogg, for to be alone is a sad thing. They say, however, that with two, ruin is easier to live with.'

'They say so, madam.'

'Mr Fogg,' said Mrs Aouda, rising and holding out her hand to the gentleman, 'do you wish to have both a relative and a friend? Will you have me for your wife?'

Mr Fogg, at this, stood up. There seemed to be an unusual look in his eyes. Mrs Aouda looked at him. It was the sweet look of a noble woman, who had dared everything to save the man who saved her life. All this flooded over Mr Fogg. He closed his eyes for a moment. When he opened them again, he simply said, 'I love you. Yes, I truly love you, and I am yours for the rest of my life.'

'Ah!' cried Mrs Aouda.

He rang for Passepartout. He came immediately. He understood at once what had happened, and his face shone with joy.

Mr Fogg asked him to go at once to the priest and organize his marriage for the next day, Monday.

It was five minutes past eight in the evening. The priest should be at home.

Passepartout went out, running as fast as he could.

What was happening at the Reform Club?

It is time to tell here what happened in England after the arrest of the real robber of the Bank of England. James Strand was the name of the man and he was arrested on 17th December.

Three days before, people had thought that Phileas Fogg was the robber. Now it was known that he was an honest gentleman making the tour of the world in eighty days.

Everyone was interested again. All the newspapers started to write about whether the eighty-day tour was possible or not. More bets were made. Everyone was excited and waited impatiently for the result. The five friends at the Reform Club passed the last three days feeling rather uneasy. Would this Phileas Fogg, whom they had forgotten, reappear before their eyes? Where was he at this moment? They had had no news from him. Was he dead?

So, on that Saturday evening, the 21st of December, there was a great crowd outside the Reform Club and in the streets nearby.

The five men from the Reform Club were gathered there. The two bankers, John Sullivan and Samuel

Fallentin,
the engineer
Andrew Stuart and the
two men from the Bank
of England, Gauthier Ralph
and Thomas Flanagan were anxiously
waiting.

At that moment the clock in the Club hall showed twenty minutes to nine. Andrew Stuart rose and said, 'Gentlemen, in twenty minutes' time we will win our bet.'

'What time did the last train come from Liverpool?' asked Thomas Flanagan.

'At twenty-three minutes past seven,' replied Gauthier Ralph, 'and the next train does not arrive until ten past midnight.'

'Well, gentlemen,' continued Andrew Stuart, 'if Phileas Fogg arrived on the train that came in at twenty-three minutes past seven, he would already be here. We must have won the bet!'

'Let us wait before deciding,' replied Samuel Fallentin. 'You know what this man is like. He is always exact about everything. He never arrives too late or too soon, and he will appear here at the exact minute, I am sure.'

'And I,' said Andrew Stuart, who was very uneasy, 'would not believe it was he if I saw him! I am sure he is lost. You know that the *China*, the only steamship he could take from New York that would get him to

Liverpool in time, arrived yesterday. He was not on it! I am sure he will be at least twenty days late!'

The five men looked at each other. Their hearts were beating rather fast. They had all taken a big risk when they made that bet. But they all appeared calm on the outside, and when Samuel Fallentin said that they should play cards, they all agreed.

The minute hand of the clock was pointing to five minutes to nine.

'There are five more minutes,' said John Sullivan.

They played a little more. Then it was three minutes to nine. The players took their cards, but their eyes were always looking at the clock.

Two minutes to nine.

The minutes seemed very long.

'One minute to nine,' said John Sullivan, in a shaking voice.

One more minute and the bet would be won! Twenty thousand pounds! Andrew Stuart and the others put down their cards! They were counting the seconds!

At the fortieth second, nothing.

At the fiftieth, still nothing!

At the fifty-fifth second, there was a roar like thunder outside. Shouts and cries sounded out.

At the fifty-seventh second, the door of the room opened, and the clock had not begun to strike, when Phileas Fogg appeared, followed by an excited crowd, which had forced its way into the Club. In his calm voice Phileas Fogg said, 'Gentlemen, here I am!'

Yes! Phileas Fogg himself!

And the clock struck nine.

You will remember that at five minutes past eight Passepartout was told to go to the priest to arrange his master's marriage for the next day. In fact the priest was and he did not return until twenty to nine. Five minutes later Passepartout rushed out of the priest's house like a madman. He ran so fast that he arrived back at the Saville Row house in three minutes. He could hardly speak.

'Today — only — Saturday.'

'What is the matter?' asked Mr Fogg.

'Sir — ' said Passepartout, 'marriage — impossible!'

'Impossible?'

'Impossible — tomorrow.'

'Why?'

'Because tomorrow is Sunday.'

'Monday,' replied Mr Fogg.

'No — today is — Saturday.'

'Saturday? Impossible!'

'Yes, yes, yes!' cried Passepartout. 'You have made a mistake of one day. We arrived twenty-four hours early, but now you only have ten minutes left!'

Passepartout dragged his master into the street and into a carriage. The driver was promised one hundred pounds if he could get to the Reform Club in time.

The clock showed one second before nine o'clock as he appeared in the main room. Phileas Fogg had made the tour of the world in eighty days!

And now, how could this man, who was always so exact, have made a mistake of one day? Why did he think that it was the evening of Saturday 21st December, when it was only Friday 20th December, only seventy-nine days since he left London?

This is the reason for his mistake. It is very simple. He had gained a day on his journey, because he had travelled towards the east. If he had travelled towards the west, he would have lost a day. Passepartout's famous watch, which had always kept London time, would have shown this, if it had shown the days as well as the minutes and the hours!

So, Phileas Fogg won the twenty thousand pounds. But he had spent nineteen thousand on his journey. He did not mind, he was not interested in the money, only in winning. He divided that remaining one thousand pounds between Passepartout and poor Detective Fix. He could not remain angry with Fix. After all, he had only been doing his duty. But, because he was an exact man, he made Passepartout pay the bill for the gaslight he left burning in his room for nineteen hundred and twenty hours.

Mr Fogg and Mrs Aouda are married

That very evening Mr Fogg, as calm as ever, said to Mrs Aouda, 'Do you still wish to be married?'

'Mr Fogg,' replied Mrs Aouda, 'it is for me to ask you that question. Before you were ruined, now you are rich.'

'Madam, my fortune belongs to you. It was because you asked me to marry you that Passepartout went to the priest. It was because of you that I learnt about my mistake.'

Their marriage took place forty-eight hours later. Passepartout was the witness.

Thus Phileas Fogg won his bet. In eighty days he had made the tour of the world! To do this he had used every kind of vehicle he could find: steamships, railways, sledges, elephants, to name a few. But then what? What had he gained by leaving home? What had he brought back from his journey? Nothing, do you say? Nothing, perhaps, except a lovely woman, who, strange as it may seem, made him the happiest of men!

Would you not, for less than that, make a tour of the world?

Questions and Activities

1 An Impossible Journey

There are eight mistakes in this description of Phileas Fogg. Find and correct them.

Phileas Fogg was an Englishman who came from London. He was a very polite man, but not a gentleman. He was rich, but he was mean with his money. He went to his club two days a week and he always arrived at a different time. He didn't have a wife or family, but he had lots of close friends. He was a man who was always in a hurry, and always looked upset.

2 Is Mr Fogg the Bank Robber?

Match the beginning of each sentence to the right ending.

1 Fix was a detective for •
2 He was at Suez to look for •
3 He knew the robber was •
4 He had to follow anyone •
5 He couldn't arrest his man •
6 He was very excited about •

• **a** the reward for success.
• **b** until a warrant arrived.
• **c** the British police.
• **d** the bank robber.
• **e** a well-dressed gentleman.
• **f** who looked suspicious.

3 India

Fill in the gaps with the words from the box.

agreed	Indian	railway	transport
determined	morning	refused	unexpectedly
elephant	nowhere	searched	village

At eight o'clock in the (1) _____ the train to
Calcutta stopped (2) _____ in the middle of
(3) _____ . The (4) _____ was not
finished. They had to find another kind of (5)
_____ . Mr Fogg and Sir Francis (6)
_____ the (7) _____ without finding
anything. Passepartout found an (8) _____
belonging to an (9) _____ man. Fogg was
(10) _____ to have him. At first the man
(11) _____ to sell, but at last he
(12) _____ .

4 Passepartout Becomes a Hero

*Put these sentences in the right order. The first one
and the last one have been done for you.*

1 They rode for two days through the forest
to Allahabad.　　　　　　　　　　　　　　[1]

2 Mr Fogg asked the guide to help them
save the girl.　　　　　　　　　　　　　　[ ]

3 She was stretched out to lie by her dead husband. ☐

4 They saw a beautiful girl being dragged along. ☐

5 Then some priests lit the wood on which the bodies lay. ☐

6 The General told Mr Fogg that it was a human sacrifice. ☐

7 Suddenly the prince rose up and picked up the girl. ☐

8 Late on the second day, they heard a strange sound. ☐

9 The next morning, the girl was dragged out of a temple. ☐

10 It was Passepartout, wearing the dead prince's clothes. [10]

5   Sent to Prison

Put the letters of these words in the right order. The first one has been done for you.

As Mr Fogg and Passepartout were (1) **ganlive** *leaving* the

railway station, a policeman (2) **harpocaped** them.

He took them to an (3) **floicfia-knoglio** building.

They were (4) **rosiperns**. At half past eight the

policeman led them into a (5) **uctormoro**. Mr Fogg

and Passepartout were (6) **scauced** of behaving

badly in a holy (7) **melpet**. It was the work of Fix,

the (8) **vitceteed**.

6   The Journey to Hong Kong

Which of these sentences are true? What is wrong with the false ones?

		T	F
1	The *Rangoon* arrived in Hong Kong a day early.	☐	☐
2	A harbour official said the *Carnatic* had already left.	☐	☐
3	Mr Fogg was already twenty-four hours behind.	☐	☐
4	Fix invited Passepartout to have a meal, and he accepted.	☐	☐
5	Fix told Passepartout he worked for the Reform Club.	☐	☐
6	He asked Passepartout to keep Mr Fogg in Hong Kong.	☐	☐
7	Fix became very drunk and smoked an opium pipe.	☐	☐
8	No one told Mr Fogg that his ship was leaving early.	☐	☐

7 Master and Servant Meet Again

Circle the right words to say what happened.

Mr Fogg offered a sailor (1) **two/one** hundred pounds

a day, and a (2) **boat/reward**, to go to Yokohama. The

sailor said it was too (3) **far/near**. He said he would

take them to Shanghai where the (4) **steamship/sailing

ship** for San Francisco (5) **stopped/started**. They had

(6) **four/five** days to get there. If the sea was

(7) **rough/calm**, and the (8) **rain/wind** kept to the

south-east, they should be able to do it.

8 The Journey across America

Put the words in brackets in the right order.

1 After three days on the train to New York, the [of]
  [sound] [was] [shooting] [heard]

  _____.

2 Indians raced along beside the moving train, [on]
  [shooting] [board] [and] [climbing]

  _____.

3 Once the train passed Fort Kearney station, it could
  [no] [from] [expect] [anyone] [help]

  _____.

4 Passepartout pulled out the iron bar between the [car] [the] [baggage] [engine] [and]

_____.

5 The train stopped and its passengers were safe, but [missing] [the] [was] [Frenchman] [brave]

_____.

9 Mr Fogg Becomes a Sea Captain

Complete the crossword puzzle. In the centre you will see the name of a ship. The first one has been done for you.

Mr Fogg went to the harbour and found a (1). Her (2) said he would take them all to (3) for (4) thousand pounds. By noon the (5) day, Mr Fogg was in (6) of the ship and the captain was (7) in his (8). They were going to (9).

10 **What Finally Happens**

Who did these things? Fill in the gaps with the names from the box. You can use some names more than once.

the driver	Fix	Passepartout
the five gentlemen	Mrs Aouda	Phileas Fogg

1 _____ threw back his arm and hit Detective Fix.

2 _____ was the reason why Phileas Fogg had lost his fortune.

3 _____ was sure that Mr Fogg would try to kill himself.

4 _____ told Mrs Aouda he loved her and would marry her.

5 _____ ran to the priest's house, to organize the marriage.

6 _____ thought Mr Fogg would not arrive in time.

7 _____ could receive one hundred pounds for getting to the Reform Club in time.

8 _____ arrived at the Reform Club just before nine o'clock.

9 _____ won twenty thousand pounds.

Whole book

What happened where? Match the place to the thing that happened there.

1 **Suez, Egypt** •

• **a** Fix arrested Mr Fogg for being a robber.

2 **Bombay, India** •

• **b** Passepartout saved Mrs Aouda from a suttee.

3 **Near Allahabad, India** •

• **c** They fought Indians and sailed on a sledge.

4 **Calcutta, India** •

• **d** Mr Fogg discovered he had gained an extra day.

5 **Hong Kong** •

• **e** Fix was looking for a robber and found Mr Fogg.

6 **Fort Kearney, USA** •

• **f** Mr Fogg lost his servant and missed his ship.

7 **Liverpool, England** •

• **g** Mr Fogg and his servant were both prisoners.

8 **London, England** •

• **h** Passepartout went into a temple and lost his shoes.

Book Report

Now write a book report to display in the library or your classroom. These questions will help you.

Title

Type What type of story is your book?

- Adventure
- Classic
- Crime
- Detective story
- Fairy tale
- Horror and suspense
- Mystery
- Play
- Romance
- Science fiction and fantasy
- Short story
- Others

Characters Who are the main characters in the book?

Main characters Describe the main characters.
What do they look like?
What are they like?

Story What is the story about?
Remember not to give the ending away!

My comments What did you think of the story?
Did you enjoy it?
Would you recommend this book to your classmates?

Visit the website and download the book report template
www.oupchina.com.hk/elt/oper

STARTER

The Ant and the Grasshopper and Other Stories by Aesop
Retold by David Foulds

The Brave Little Tailor and Other Stories by the Brothers Grimm
Retold by Katherine Mattock

The Emperor's New Clothes and Other Stories by Hans Christian Andersen
Retold by Janice Tibbetts

Folk Tales from Around the World
Retold by Rosemary Border

Giants, Dragons and Other Magical Creatures
Retold by Philip Popescu

Heroes and Heroines
Retold by Philip Popescu

In the Land of the Gods
Retold by Magnus Norberg

Journey to the West
Retold by Rosemary Border

The Lion and the Mouse and Other Stories by Aesop
Retold by David Foulds

The Little Mermaid and Other Stories by Hans Christian Andersen
Retold by Janice Tibbetts

The Monkey King
Retold by Rosemary Border

Peter Pan
Retold by Katherine Mattock